A Candlelight Ecstasy Romance ®

**"DID I MENTION WHEN WE TALKED
THIS MORNING THAT I'M IN LOVE WITH
YOU?" ROSS SAID, VERY GENTLY.**

"No, you didn't, and I guess I didn't say it either,
but I am," Ellen sighed.

"That's good to know, honey," he said quietly.
"Maybe someday . . ."

"I haven't got time to wait for *someday*!" Ellen
said crossly. "I want you now, and I want your
babies now, and furthermore, I want to live on your
ranch with you now! You mark my words, you'll be
sorry *someday* when you find out what you've
passed up! It's time I got married again and started
a family and that's exactly what I'm going to do! So,
so long, Ross Sayer. See you around . . . *someday*!"

A CANDLELIGHT ECSTASY ROMANCE ®

A TIME
TO LOVE

Jackie Black

A CANDLELIGHT ECSTASY ROMANCE ®

Published by
Dell Publishing Co., Inc.
1 Dag Hammarskjold Plaza
New York, New York 10017

Dell ® TM 681510, Dell Publishing Co., Inc.

Candlelight Ecstasy Romance®, 1,203,540, is a registered
trademark of Dell Publishing Co., Inc.,
New York, New York.

ISBN: 0-440-18670-6

Printed in the United States of America
First printing—November 1983

To Our Readers:

We have been delighted with your enthusiastic response to Candlelight Ecstasy Romances®, and we thank you for the interest you have shown in this exciting series.

In the upcoming months we will continue to present the distinctive sensuous love stories you have come to expect only from Ecstasy. We look forward to bringing you many more books from your favorite authors and also the very finest work from new authors of contemporary romantic fiction.

As always, we are striving to present the unique, absorbing love stories that you enjoy most—books that are more than ordinary romance.

Your suggestions and comments are always welcome. Please write to us at the address below.

Sincerely,

The Editors
Candlelight Romances
1 Dag Hammarskjold Plaza
New York, New York 10017

CHAPTER ONE

"Come on, Ellie, say yes. You know you need a break."
Rosalynd Turner's always positive tone was now a combination of coaxing and bullying, and her alert brown eyes fairly commanded Ellen Bowman to give in.

Ellen tucked an errant strand of silky brown hair behind one ear and faced her friend with a wry lack of enthusiasm in her clear, hazel eyes. "Sure, I could use a break, Rosie," she admitted dryly, "but going on a ski trip with you and the rest of the gang and trying to pretend I'm enjoying it as much as I did when John was alive is not my idea of a break." She shrugged and turned to stare out the window at the white-blanketed countryside, and her tone was wistful as she added, "Besides, I'd feel like a fifth wheel. I'm not part of a couple anymore, Rosie, and this is a couples' trip."

"Nonsense!" was Rosie's crisp reply. "This is a get-together for friends, and you're certainly that!" She eyed Ellen cautiously for a second before she added very casually, "And you won't be making an odd number, either, because Ross Sayer is coming too."

At hearing that, Ellen's head jerked around, an expression of disgust pulling her generous mouth down at one corner. "Oh, great!" she said sarcastically. "That's one hell of an inducement!"

Rosie shook her flyaway auburn curls with impatience.

7

"Come on, Ellie!" she said, disapproval redolent in her tone. "I didn't say you had to be his partner or anything. I just said the numbers would be even!"

"You can just bet we wouldn't be partners!" Ellen said with more sarcasm. "He doesn't like me any more than I like him." Then she looked at her friend in puzzlement. "Why is he going by himself anyway? Where's Tina?"

Rosie threw up her hands in disgust. "Ellie Bowman, don't you ever listen to anything anymore? I told you four months ago that Tina had left Ross. She got a Reno divorce and took off with some rich foreigner." And at Ellen's wide-eyed look of astonishment, followed by a curving smile she didn't even try to hide, Rosalynd chided her sternly. "That's rotten of you, Ellie. Ross took it very hard!"

For a moment, Ellen considered trying to seem repentant, then gave up the idea as blatant hypocrisy. "Serves him right," she said unfeelingly instead. "He married her for her looks and that empty little-girl charm. And that's all he got and, in my opinion, all he deserved."

"Ellie, Ellie." Rosie shook her head with impatient sadness. "You're not ever going to forgive Ross for what you overheard him say about you and John, are you?" And at Ellen's defiant glare, she said softly, "That was a long time ago, honey, and he said it before he thought. I'm sure he soon found out how wrong he was."

"Ha! Don't bet on it!" Ellen objected, crossing her arms over the soft green of her cashmere sweater. "He's such a macho man, I can't imagine him admitting he was ever wrong about anything!"

Rosalynd shrugged and gave up. "Well, I like him a lot, Ellie. I always have. So did John. You would, too, if you gave him a chance, but"—she held up her hands to ward off another protest from Ellen—"that's not really important. You two can avoid each other to your heart's con-

8

tent, just like you always do. The important thing is that you get out of that bookstore for a while and do something that's fun for a change."

Rosalynd's full red lips softened in sympathy as she saw the restless, trapped look come into Ellen's eyes at mention of the bookstore. It had been John's store, his pride and joy, his lifelong dream. She knew Ellen kept it open and slaved over it now for the sake of John's memory, though she was entirely unsuited for such an occupation and would have been much happier digging ditches— anything so long as it was outdoor work and physical— rather than being cooped up among shelves of books. It wasn't even as though Ellen had to work at all. With her inheritance—the inheritance that had made it possible for John to have his store in the first place—she could have played for the rest of her life without lifting a finger in gainful employment. But Rosalynd knew that sort of idleness would never suit Ellen, even as she wondered how long it was going to take for Ellen to get over her martyrlike compulsion to maintain John's dream at the cost of her own happiness.

"I'll be really hurt if you don't come, Ellen," Rosalynd said now, making the effort to seem sulky when it was against her entire nature. But she was prepared to fudge quite a bit in an attempt to jar Ellen out of her grief . . . and more important, out of that damned bookstore for a while!

"Why, Rosie . . ." Ellen looked surprised and puzzled at seeing her normally sunny-natured friend looking petulant and hurt. "Why should it matter so much to you whether I . . ."

"Because I'm sick and tired of never seeing anything of you anymore," Rosie said grumpily. "I thought we were friends, but we might as well live clear across the country from each other. I'm always the one who calls you, and

9

I'm always the one who comes to see you. Maybe I should just take the hint and stop doing either. You don't act as if you care."

To Rosalynd's secret glee, Ellen was on her feet and across the room in an instant to wrap her arms around her friend, her hazel eyes wide and anxious with concern. "Rosie, that's not true! You know it's not! You and Jake are my closest friends! I don't know what I would have done without you in the past six months!"

"Hmph!" Rosie pouted as convincingly as she could manage. "So you say. But you sure haven't been acting like it lately."

"Ah, Rosie, I'm sorry." Ellen sighed with self-disgust as she gave Rosie another hug. "I know I haven't been easy to be around since John—"

Rosie interrupted, not wanting Ellen to turn her thoughts to John again right then. "You haven't been around much at all," she pointed out crisply. "That's the point." She shrugged, trying to look forlorn. "I guess it doesn't matter to you that *I* won't have as much fun on this trip if you're not along."

As she had hoped, this last was the clincher. Ellen had the softest heart of anyone Rosie knew where her friends and loved ones were concerned, and Rosie didn't feel even a twinge guilty at playing blatantly on that softheartedness, since she considered it to be in Ellen's best interests.

"Okay, okay!" Ellen gave in hastily. "I'll close the store for a week if Janie can't work for me, if it's that important to you that I come. Just don't make me feel like a louse anymore, Rosie! I *hate* feeling like this!"

Rosie turned one of her brightest, sunniest smiles on Ellen then, her manner changing 180 degrees now that she had what she wanted. "Why, honey, I didn't mean to make you feel like a louse," she protested innocently, batting huge brown eyes in astonishment.

Ellen eyed her friend suspiciously. "You could have fooled me," she said with wry doubtfulness. "Anyway, forget it," she said as she saw Rosie preparing to defend herself again. "Just tell me the details so I can start getting ready for this trip you're so determined I take."

And as Rosie did so, Ellen was surprised to find herself becoming interested and enthusiastic about breaking her gloomy routine for a while, even though underneath there was still the feeling of guilt and longing because she was alive to make such plans while her beloved, adored husband was gone forever, leaving an empty space in her life she was certain would never be filled again.

CHAPTER TWO

Characteristically, Ellen was with the men at the back of the van helping to load the luggage and gear, while the other three women chatted and waited until it was time to go. Ellen moved to pick up a large ice chest containing the meat they were taking with them, but as she bent to grasp the handles, two large, gloved hands beat her to it.

"I'll get it," Ross Sayer said in a cool, distant tone. "It's too heavy for you to lift."

Ellen tensed, took a deep breath to control her temper, then stood up to gaze with bland unconcern into the ice-blue eyes of the man facing her. "Suit yourself, Tarzan," she tossed off with lackadaisical irony. "We sure wouldn't want me to get a hernia, would we?"

"Why not?" he came back at her without a moment's hesitation. "If you're determined to act like a man, you have to be prepared to accept the penalties as well."

Ellen just stopped herself from retorting that at least she had been able to keep the love of her spouse, which was something *he* hadn't been able to do, but her sense of fair play decided that was below the belt, so instead she gritted her teeth and turned her back on the one friend of John's she had never had any desire to turn into a friend of her own. Ever since the day she had overheard him remarking to Rosalynd and Jake that he was disappointed in John at marrying for money, just as though he considered it impossible John could have had any other reason for marrying an almost plain, certainly tomboyish female, she had quite literally hated Ross Sayer's guts, and she didn't expect that situation to change any in the near future, if ever!

As she climbed into the van and slid down on her spine to stare stonily out the window, Ellen knew she was over-reacting to Ross, but for the life of her, she couldn't help it. He was a stone-age, chauvinistic, insensitive pig, in her opinion, all wrapped up in an outer shell so handsomely appealing that most women failed to pick up on the fact that there was little worth having on the inside. She grimaced disgustedly as she remembered the woman he had finally deemed worthy of carrying his name—an empty-headed, beautiful showcase who was as pathetically incapable of developing any real character as he was!

"Come on, everybody, climb in!" Jake Turner called out in an exuberant voice, interrupting Ellen's train of thought momentarily and making her smile as the man himself, looking as roly-poly as Santa Claus in his red ski jacket, climbed into the driver's seat of the van. He hitched around to give her a beaming grin and reached back to pat her bluejean-clad knee affectionately. "All set, babe?" he inquired cheerfully.

"All set, Jake," she responded with equal cheeriness, determined not to let her personal differences with Ross Sayer spoil this trip for anyone else. Her resolve took a setback, however, when Ross, the last to enter the van, pulled open the door beside her and paused expectantly for her to slide over. She did so grudgingly, though she was fuming inside at the thought of having to sit beside him during the long drive to Colorado. Besides, she liked the window seat, and now *he* had it!

She turned determinedly to Peg Daimler on her right and inquired about Peg's new baby boy with an interest

13

that was only partly assumed. Ellen adored children, and her one biggest regret in life was that she and John had waited too long to start a family. But then they had thought they had all the time they needed . . . not only to have children, but for a lot of other things as well. And they had been so very, very wrong.

Even a new mother could run down after a while, however, and Peg, as a result of too many late night feedings, was soon yawning and snuggling up against the other door to take a short nap, while Ellen was forced to face forward and hope to start a conversation with someone else, either in the front seat where Jake, Rosalynd, and Peg's husband, Randy, sat, or behind her where Bill and Marie Boyer were.

Out of the corner of her eye she saw that Ross was turning from his contemplation of the countryside speeding by to regard her with unrevealing speculation. She had thought he hadn't heard the conversation between her and Peg, but she was proven wrong when he tossed a question at her in a smoothly bland voice.

"Why didn't you and John ever have any children, Ellen? I know John always wanted kids."

Ellen stiffened, then gave an inner sigh of resignation. Of course, Ross *would* think it was her fault there hadn't been any children, and she had no intention of explaining that it was more John's decision. He had been too caught up in his bookstore to want any distractions for a while.

She turned and smiled with sweet blandness right back at Ross, ignoring his question in favor of one of her own. "Why didn't you and Tina have any, Ross? John always said you wanted kids too."

His eyes narrowed warningly at her, giving him a predatory look that almost made her shudder. His was a rough-hewn, masculine face saved from harshness only by the almost tender curve of a generous mouth which he seemed

14

to be trying to hide behind the thick growth of a gray-streaked mustache. His thick blond hair showed no sign of matching gray as yet, however, and his blue eyes held a clarity that was startling and discomforting in some mysterious manner.

He shrugged his huge, masculine shoulders beneath the blue ski jacket he wore. "The best laid plans . . ." he said off-handedly, his tone revealing nothing.

"Yes," Ellen agreed with a bleak shortness, turning her face away before he could see the vulnerable trembling of her mouth. She was thinking that all of her best laid plans—and John's—had gone so astray there was no chance whatsoever of their getting back on track.

"You didn't answer me," Ross said so softly Ellen doubted anyone else heard.

In fact, she was incapable of answering now, so she merely shrugged, then leaned forward to tap Rosalynd on the shoulder. "Did you remember to bring napkins?" she asked in a carefully unrevealing voice.

But when Rosalynd swung around to face her, she immediately saw the sad, bleak look in Ellen's green-tinged hazel eyes and knew at once her friend was in need of rescue. "Sure I did," she said cheerfully. "You know I've got the memory of an elephant," and then she rushed on in an infectious voice that no one could resist. "Say, speaking of elephants, did you hear the one about . . ." And she went on to tell a joke that had everyone roaring with laughter in a matter of seconds.

From there she went on to lead the group in a round of singing that effectively restored Ellen's humor and relaxed her to the extent that she could even, grudgingly, take pleasure in the deep baritone of Ross's surprisingly good singing voice.

After that, Ellen indulged in idle chatter with Bill Boyer about a new pair of skis he was dying to try out, before

15

she began yawning herself and settled back as comfortably as she could to take a nap. Sometime later, in reaction to a slight swerve of the van, she swam up from a deep sleep to a half-awake state to find herself cuddled snugly against a masculine chest she thought, in reaction to a dream she'd been having, was John's. She had taken off her gloves, and her hands were freezing, so with impatient fumbling she wriggled and maneuvered until she had one hand up under the coat in the back, and the other inside the coat in the front. Giving him a little squeeze of appreciation for the accommodating movements he had made to help her, she snuggled her head against his neck, gave him a sleepy kiss there, mumbled "Thanks, honey," and prepared to drift back into a deeper sleep.

The amused answer, "You're welcome, sweetheart," delivered in a very low, very masculine, very un-John-like voice, stilled her last little squirm in mid-effort and brought her eyes open with a jerk! Never had she been so glad in her life that the day had faded into darkness, concealing the slow, hot tide of color that was creeping into her face as though a blowtorch had been applied! She made an involuntary choking sound that Ross Sayer immediately covered up with the simple expedient of placing his hand over her mouth.

"Shhh . . ." he said quietly, still with that same amused tone in his voice. "Everyone but Jake is asleep, and though he's been watching us in the rearview mirror for the last fifteen minutes, he's very discreet. If you'll keep quiet, no one will know we're cuddling back here like a couple of teenagers."

Stiffening, Ellen made a move to jerk upright, but Ross's arms tightened, keeping her where she was. "You know," he whispered, a silent rumble of laughter in his chest, "I think I've been wrong about you. You feel a hell of a lot more feminine than I ever suspected."

Temper and embarrassment swamping her good sense, Ellen hissed back at him in a furious whisper. "I *am* a hell of a lot more woman than you'd ever know what to do with, Ross Sayer! Now, let me go!"

To her surprise and chagrin, Ross didn't answer her challenge in words. Instead, he shifted slightly to bring her full up against his body, his arms tightening to still her instinctive protesting movement. Since her own arms were trapped under his coat, there was little she could do short of howling out her sense of outrage to everyone in the van, and she would have died rather than risk the teasing that would surely follow such an exhibition!

She almost yelped as she felt the long length of his powerfully muscled leg come up between her own, but even if she had gotten the yelp out, Ross's mouth would have smothered it before it was half-uttered. She inhaled sharply as she felt his mouth close over hers, the silky tendrils of his mustache providing a shield for both their mouths and giving a shuddering intimacy to his kiss that Ellen would have sworn was impossible. Then his tongue was trying to force entry, and when it met only teeth, Ross shifted his mouth slightly to give her a stinging little bite on her lower lip that had her opening her mouth immediately to give voice to another protest. Instantly the tongue darted in, the protest was strangled, and Ellen was subjected to a sensuous invasion that despite all her best efforts to deny it started a fire inside her that was fed by the pressure of Ross's leg inside her thighs and by the bulging heat of his arousal she could feel pressed against her. She gave an involuntary shudder, then went completely limp for the duration of the kiss.

When Ross finally raised his head, she felt his breath on her face, coming in the labored effort of a man in the grip of strong passion. "Don't challenge me like that too often, honey," he gritted out in a whisper at her ear. "We're both

17

too damned hungry to keep out of trouble for very long if you do."

She didn't misunderstand him. She couldn't even dispute him. She was shocked to the core to find that her normal sensual nature, which John had honed to a fine balance, could explode on her like that with a man she didn't even like! "I . . . won't . . . !" she reassured him in a low, shaking voice, then shivered with withdrawal pains as he silently and smoothly withdrew his leg from between hers and released her from his arms.

She sat up quietly, hugging her arms around herself, afraid to move too much for fear of waking Peg, who still slept on beside her. She faced forward, staring unseeingly out through the front windshield, wishing she could drop right through the floor of the van and disappear out of sight forever! She almost jumped out of her skin when Ross lifted a hand to place it on her neck under the silken swatch of her long brown hair and rub reassuringly. It was an understanding, comforting gesture, as though he knew about the conflict raging inside her and wanted her to go easy on herself. That he could make such a gesture—indeed, that he could be sensitive enough to realize that one was needed—threw her into an even greater state of inner turmoil. She would have sworn he didn't have one empathetic bone in his whole magnificent body!

By the time they stopped on the road for a late dinner, Ellen had recovered most of her composure, outwardly at least, though she was pale, and her wide, clear hazel eyes held a rather staring look, as though she were looking off into the distance somewhere trying to define an enigma. She did have presence of mind enough to try to respond naturally to anyone who spoke to her, and to be grateful that Ross gave no sign that anything had happened between them. He ignored her, just as he always had in the past, and she took pains to sit as far away from him as possible in the tiny restaurant where they ate. When it was time to return to the van, she managed to ask Randy, quite naturally, if he would mind if she sat in the front, while he sat beside his wife, explaining that she was feeling a little carsick, which was an out-and-out lie. Her inner queasiness had nothing whatsoever to do with motion sickness.

They arrived at the condominium they'd rented on the outskirts of Winter Park around midnight, and Ellen threw herself into helping to unload the van again, though she took care to stay out of Ross's way. When the only thing left in the van was the cooler of meat Ross had refused to let her lift earlier, Ellen, in a fit of rebellion, and since she was the only one left outside at the moment, bent to pick it up with all the confidence in her own strength she normally held.

"Oof!" she grunted as the damned thing barely moved. It seemed it was a lot heavier than she'd realized, but she was determined it wouldn't defeat her . . . or rather that Ross Sayer wouldn't! So she scooted the thing to the edge of the back entrance of the van and climbed out, then turned back to try once again to lift it. Then she felt a light swat on her bottom and heard Ross's voice, which this time was affectionately amused.

"That has a good portion of one of my best steers in it, honey, and it about gives *me* a hernia to lift it, so back off, okay? You can chop wood or something tomorrow to get back your manly pride."

Ellen glared at him, hating the laughter in his blue eyes, despising his attitude, loathing his sense of humor . . . or lack of it! "Great!" she said flatly. "Just make sure you're not anywhere around while I have the ax in my hand!" She could have killed him when, as she swung her back to him to stomp to the condominium, she heard his burst of absolutely spontaneous, gratingly masculine, laughter behind her.

She managed to clear her expressive face of any sign of anger as she helped the other three women put away the food they'd brought, but she was wholeheartedly grateful that it was so late, and that everyone was ready for bed once that task was accomplished. The condominium had five bedrooms, so she had a tiny room of her own, but she was less than pleased to learn that Ross's room was directly opposite hers. However, she managed to avoid him successfully, and before long, she had on her long, flannel, rosy pink pajamas with the feet in them and was climbing between the sheets.

After some deep thinking about what had happened between her and Ross in the van, she finally managed to come to peace with herself. It was just as Ross had said. She *was* sexually hungry, though she hadn't been aware of it until he had pointed it out to her so drastically. And regardless of how much she disliked Ross, he was a gorgeous specimen of manhood, so perhaps it wasn't too surprising that she had reacted so completely to him. Besides, she'd been half asleep.

Not to worry, she told herself as she flopped over onto her stomach and gave a huge yawn. She'd make darned sure it didn't happen again, and no doubt her reawakened appetites would die a natural death once she got back into her usual routine. Meanwhile, she would enjoy the skiing and the company of the rest of her friends, and she knew from experience she would be much too tired to lie awake fretting about what had happened for the rest of her stay here. And it was going to be easier now that Ross was giving every indication he was back to his old nasty self.

The next morning Ellen sat up groggily in her bed. It was very early, but she needed to use the bathroom desperately, and thinking it would be safe to make a quick trip and get back into her room before anyone else was up, she didn't even bother with a robe. Her all-over pajamas were as unrevealing as anyone could wish anyway. She always wore them on ski trips because she suffered from cold feet, and John had been jerked awake by their icy touch enough times that he had been downright grateful when she had adopted her present sleepwear on their trips here.

Her eyes were half closed and she was pulling a curl of tangled brown hair out of her left eye when she pulled open the door of her room to step out into the hallway. At that moment the door directly opposite her own opened as well, and Ross Sayer stood there half naked, his sleepy, bedroom blue eyes beginning to open in astonishment as he took in the sight of Ellen glaring groggily at him as she stood encased from neck to toe in her fuzzy pink pajamas with her hair in wild disarray all over her head. Then his astonishment turned to all-out helpless laughter that shook his whole very large, very masculine frame as he collapsed against the door to support himself as he roared. Fortunately, he was making an effort to keep his roar to a minimum volume so as not to wake up the whole household, but Ellen was in no mood to appreciate his consideration for the others, when he was being decidedly ungentlemanly where she was concerned.

Never at her most tactful in the morning anyway, Ellen said the first thing that came into her mind. "You're no vision of loveliness either, you fink!" she snarled at him as she turned away to head toward the bathroom. But even in her present mood she knew she was being less than truthful. He might not be a vision of loveliness, but he was sure as hell the epitome of sexy manliness in his bare chest and low-slung pajama bottoms!

She felt his powerful hand on her shoulder an instant later, and it was all she could do to keep from bringing her

21

fists up in a boxing stance, which would have been patently ridiculous, as she didn't know the first thing about
boxing. But she wished she did, and her face showed it as
she scowled up at him.

"I'm sorry," he said, trying to sound apologetic and
failing since he was still grinning all over his face as he
looked her over. "I just wasn't ready for . . . that is, you
took me by surprise . . . I mean . . ." He started laughing
again and Ellen longed to take a swipe at his handsome
face! She considered it downright unfair that he could
manage to look even more attractive than he normally was
when his blond hair was tousled, there were marks of a
pillow crease on one side of his weather-tanned face, and
his eyes were still sleepily groggy, while she knew she must
look even *more* of a mess than she normally did first thing
in the morning!

Well, if she couldn't beat him, she would join him, she
decided grimly. "Now you know why John and I never
had any children," she said with deadly sweetness before
jerking her shoulder out from under his grip and storming
off to finish her trip to the bathroom.

Once her business was finished there, she paused to look
glumly into the small mirror over the sink, reflecting that
she had been entirely right. She did look a mess, at least
to her own eyes. She was entirely blind to the fact that her
pouting mouth looked exquisitely kissable, her sleepy
hazel eyes held a combination of sweet vulnerability and
bedroom come-hitherness, and her hair, even in all its
disarray, was a luxurious mass that had made more than
one man long to see it spread out on a white pillowcase.

Giving a resigned sigh, she peeked out the door to make
sure the coast was clear, then scurried back to her room
as fast as her legs would take her. Once there, she knew
she wasn't going to be able to sleep again, so she dressed
in tight yellow ski pants and a green sweater, then brushed

22

on some rouge, pulled a comb through her hair, tied it back in a ponytail, and made her way to the kitchen to start breakfast for the others.

She had bacon frying, coffee perking, and was beating a huge bowl of pancake batter to within an inch of its life when Ross appeared in the kitchen, looking stunningly attractive in his blue ski outfit that matched his eyes. Ellen looked up long enough to glower at him before returning her attention to her bowl of batter. He poured himself a cup of coffee, then came to stand at her side.

"I am sorry, Ellen," he said quietly, though his voice was not overly apologetic, just factual. Then it turned teasing as he murmured, "Though if I hadn't had my arms full of you yesterday and didn't know what's under those clothes, I might believe what you said about children."

Ellen bristled, both at his reminder of what had happened between them in the van and his reference to what had happened this morning. The man had the tact of a bull in a china shop, she thought wrathfully, then grew even more angry when he continued to add insult to injury.

"But why in the hell *do* you sleep in that getup? If you get cold, wouldn't a flannel gown do just as well? I haven't seen one of those outfits on anyone over the age of three in my life!"

Very carefully, Ellen set down the bowl of pancake batter, then turned to glare up at Ross's features with hands on her hips. "My feet get cold," she gritted out at him with exaggerated patience. "And if adults weren't meant to wear something like that, they wouldn't make them in my size, would they? Now, if we're through discussing my sleeping attire, would you kindly wake up the others so we can start breakfast?"

He looked down at her speculatively for a moment before a gleam of wickedness appeared in his startling blue eyes. "Come sleep in my bed tonight, and I'll warm your

23

feet for you, honey," he purred at her in a low, sexy growl that brought a gasp of outrage to her lips. But there was something like confused wariness in her eyes as well, and, at seeing it, Ross looked smugly satisfied before he turned away to do as she'd asked.

That smugness confirmed something she had only suspected before—that Ross Sayer was beginning to take an unholy enjoyment in provoking both her anger and her very feminine fear of him as a man . . . a man with very virile, very basic needs. She relaxed at that realization, feeling relieved that his sudden interest in her really had nothing to do with the interest a man would show in a woman who attracted him, but was rather the mischievousness of the little boy inside the man, a very nasty little boy, in her opinion!

Well, she knew how to deal with that! she thought with some smugness of her own. Her predictable reactions merely spurred him on. Therefore, she would cease to react predictably. And, feeling much better than she had at any time since the trip had started, she grabbed up the bowl of batter and dipped a generous cupful of the stuff to pour onto the heated griddle of the stove.

CHAPTER THREE

Ellen was even more glad she'd come as she sped down a steep slope on her skis later that morning. It was a glorious day—cold, clear, and sunny, and the snow was just the way she liked it. It felt heavenly to be using her muscles and her body like this in the outdoors again, and her eyes were gleaming with the first happiness they had held in over six months.

She was a damned good skier, even if she did say so herself, and she fairly flew over the slope, feeling so exhilarated she felt like bursting into happy laughter. Instead, she merely grinned as she passed Randy and Peg, then Rosalynd and Jake, then Bill and Marie, to speed on downward with the ease of a born skier.

She recognized Ross's blue outfit farther down the hill, and felt a thrill of challenge as she saw that though he hadn't let out all stops, he was showing the form of a skier who came close to her own expertise. Ha! she thought with satisfied smugness. This was one area where she could save her "manly pride," as he put it with a vengeance, and she put all her skill to work as she caught up with, then passed him, flashing him a superior grin in the process.

That grin was a mistake, she realized a few moments later, as he passed her with an ease and gracefulness that managed to give the impression he was out for a Sunday stroll instead of a crusade to show her her place as the weaker of the species! But he made the same mistake she had, flashing a grin as he passed her, sparking her to pull out all stops.

The race was on, and even through her irritation that she couldn't seem to take and keep the lead no matter how hard she tried, Ellen felt so good at making the effort that by the time they were nearing the bottom of the hill she didn't even mind when Ross zipped by her one last time to make a breathtaking, beautifully executed stop before he looked up to watch her descent.

She slowed then, taking her time and, unaware how graceful she looked, she coasted to a stop beside him, flung off her goggles and laughed delightedly up at him. "That was great!" she chortled uninhibitedly. "You can damned well ski, Ross Sayer!"

His eyes were mocking, with something else moving behind their clear blue depths that Ellen couldn't identify as he dipped his head to acknowledge her compliment. "So can you," he said with dry approbation. "Did John teach you?"

Ellen opened her mouth to protest, then, remembering her resolve of earlier that morning, she merely smiled at him with bland friendliness. "Nope, I've been skiing since I was three," she informed him cheerfully. "Want to do it again?"

Ross's eyes were hooded as he studied her. "How are you at moguls?" he inquired politely.

Ellen waggled her hand to indicate so-so, but there was a wicked gleam in her hazel eyes that made Ross's gaze sharpen perceptively. "I get by," she said innocently.

"Let's go then," Ross said with a bland inflection, and the two of them pushed off to go to the lift together.

He beat her there, too, of course, but not by so much that she didn't feel comfortably complacent that she had held her own, and she was more cheerful than she had been for quite some time when they joined the others at the lodge for a cup of hot chocolate. This was the way to handle an old stick-in-the-mud chauvinist like Ross Sayer, she was thinking with relaxed satisfaction as she seated herself beside Rosie and Jake. Keep her cool, keep her good sportsmanship while making him work very hard to maintain his attitude that a woman couldn't compete with a man in some things, and let his little barbs roll right off her like water off a duck's back.

"You're looking very pleased with yourself," Rosalynd commented with a great deal of satisfaction as she eyed the sparkling clarity in Ellen's eyes, the healthy pink in her cheeks, and the cheerful smile on her lips. "How come? Did you manage to dump Ross in a snowdrift once or twice while you two were burning up the slopes?"

Ellen giggled and shoved Rosie with an arm in her ribs. "No, but I sure gave him a run for his money," she replied with happy smugness. "I'll bet his poor little old ego is really hanging around his knees right about now!"

Rosalynd lifted her brows as she swung her head to the other end of the table where Ross sat looking as relaxed and comfortable and undamaged as he ever had, while a stunning, feminine-looking little woman at the next table flirted with him outrageously. "His ego looks all right to me," Rosie commented dryly.

Ellen followed her gaze, took in the situation in a glance, and snorted her disbelief. "Look at that!" she said with mild, disgusted resignation. "He'll never learn, will he? That babe looks like Tina's twin. Wouldn't you think he'd give up his prejudices where women are concerned after his experiences with that vapid little vampire he married?" She shrugged and shook her head. "I'll bet he needs someone like that to make him feel like a big man. He sure has trouble coping with a woman who can meet him on his own level."

She wished she'd kept her mouth shut, when Rosie swung her discerning brown eyes back in her direction, interested speculation gleaming in them. "Meaning you, I suppose?" she asked innocently.

Ellen stopped herself from squirming uncomfortably and kept her tone bland when she answered. "Yep. He thinks I'm one of those frustrated females who would rather have been born male. It would never enter his head that I'm not really interested in competition, just in being let alone to do what I like best as well as I'm able. He deals in stereotypes, that man!"

Rosie's gleam didn't dissipate at Ellen's easy explanation, however, though she was wise enough to drop her eyes to her cup to conceal her expression. "You mean he can't see that just because a woman tries to beat the pants off him on the ski slopes, it doesn't make her any less feminine?" she asked with further innocence.

Ellen frowned in reaction to that and glanced at Rosie thoughtfully. "Well, to be honest, I guess he is one person that brings out my competitive streak. I keep wanting to teach him a lesson!"

"What sort of lesson?" Rosie persisted, keeping her tone carefully bland.

Ellen answered with a scowl. "That just because a woman isn't a helpless little flutterer, it doesn't mean she's any less a woman," she said flatly, her good mood beginning to dissipate.

"Now, why should you care whether he thinks of you as a woman," Rosie said with gentle affection. "I thought you didn't like him."

"I don't!" Ellen asserted, trying to put conviction into her voice. "I just can't stand that sort of attitude from anyone, and if he keeps it up, he's going to end up with another Tina for his pains. If he had half a brain, he'd know no woman like that is going to want to spend her

28

days out on that ranch of his without a beauty parlor or a dress shop within ten miles!"

Rosalynd's voice was very offhand as she commented lazily, "Yes, he'd be a lot better off marrying someone like you who loves the out of doors and animals and isn't a bit afraid of hard work—yet who looks like a living dream in an evening gown and high heels, makeup, and a stylish hairdo."

Ellen cast a suspicious glance at her friend. "Was that a compliment?" she asked. "Or are you up to your matchmaking tricks, because if you are, I can tell you right now I'm not in the least—"

Rosalynd cut her off with a waving hand of dismissal and a pooh-poohing expression. "It was a compliment, you dunce," she said drawlingly. "I wouldn't dream of trying to fix the two of you up. You're both as stubborn as mules and every bit as dense sometimes."

"Well, thanks a lot," Ellen muttered, then relented as she saw Rosie's infectious smile. "You sure have a way with lefthanded compliments, Rosie. I'll say that for you." She smiled back.

"I just like to keep everybody's feet on the ground," Rosie said with a mischievous lack of repentance. "Now, are you ready to go back outside? You promised to take me up on the intermediate slope and work with me today, remember?"

Ellen agreed happily and spent a pleasant two hours with Rosie before they all piled back into the van to return to the condominium and have some lunch. Since everyone else was groaning with sore muscles and fatigue, she offered to fix the sandwiches and soup, then tensed a little as Ross, who seemed to be suffering no aftereffects from his strenuous morning, followed her into the kitchen to help her.

"It's women's work, you know." She couldn't resist

getting at him, though she kept a straight face and managed to sound innocent.

He slanted a lazy look down at her as he went to the refrigerator to rummage for condiments. "Who says?" he came back at her complacently. "It seems to me some of the greatest chefs in the world are male."

"Who says?" she mocked him, her tone and expression deadpan. "Some of those same male chefs?"

To her surprise, he laughed easily and replied, "Probably." And then he showed her that he was no stranger to a kitchen himself by helping her put together a mountain of sandwiches with deft precision.

After lunch, almost everyone wanted a nap, which seemed to be a sound idea in light of the altitude and the unaccustomed physical exercise they'd indulged in that morning, but Ellen, after lying on her back in the middle of her bed for a while, became convinced she wasn't going to be able to sleep, and hopped up to go in search of something to do.

She investigated the woodpile by the large stone fireplace in the living room and, finding the supply pretty meager, slung on her ski jacket to tramp outside to look for the storage pile. She found it out back, but at seeing most of the logs were really too big to fit easily into the fireplace, grabbed up an old rusty ax propped nearby and set to work to split some of them.

She was complacently aware she wasn't doing a very good job of it, but since she was having a good time trying, she kept at it until she heard the crack of a twig behind her and swung around to find Ross coming up, shaking his head with disgust at what she was accomplishing. *Steady,* she told herself, keeping a tight rein on her temper.

When he reached her side, Ross merely held out his hand for the ax, and Ellen hesitated, then handed it over, realizing she didn't have the fortitude to stand there and

30

hack the wood into jagged pieces with him standing there watching her. But she wasn't averse to subjecting his efforts to an intense scrutiny as he started to work with a will. He had tossed off his ski jacket, and his powerful arm and shoulder muscles fairly rippled under his plaid woolen shirt, providing Ellen with some rather absorbing if disturbing entertainment as she stood with arms folded, watching him make clean, precise strokes that put hers to shame.

He paused once to glance at her, his brows lifting as though he waited for her approbation.

"You do that very well," she said grudgingly, her tone not particularly complimentary. Then she felt ashamed of her pettiness and added, "Better than I do . . ." She gestured at the poor, mutilated pieces she'd done before he got there, her expression rueful.

"I've had a lot of practice," he said easily, sounding neither egotistical nor condemnatory of her own efforts. "I like a good fire at home, and there's a stand of trees near the river, so I do this regularly."

Ellen had been to his ranch once with John, and she loved the treeless hills called the Flint Hills in Kansas, which were used for pasturing cattle. "You're lucky you've got some trees," she said spontaneously. "But too many of them would spoil that gorgeous country, wouldn't they?"

Ross cast a speculative look at her, his blue eyes warming with appreciation of her compliment. "You like that country?" he asked casually.

Ellen nodded, then stretched her arms up high lazily as she admired the scenery around them. "I like this, too, though," she said with a natural, easy smile. "Every place has its charm."

"Umm-hmm . . ." Ross said absently as he brought the

31

ax down for another stroke. "John said once you were the outdoor type."

Ellen shrugged, refusing to comment, not sure she liked the thought of John and Ross discussing her. She knew that John had loved her with utter certainty, but she couldn't help wondering if that had come across when he talked about her to this man who assumed John had married her for her money. Perhaps because of that, an imp seized her, and she asked with perfect innocence, "Did Tina like the ranch?"

Ross didn't answer her for a moment and she saw a muscle twitch in his jaw, making her feel a little guilty for probing at what must still be a raw wound for him. But when he glanced up at her, his expression was unrevealing. "Apparently not," he said dryly, and then surprised her by adding, ". . . or maybe it was just me she didn't like. It was hard to tell what went on in her head about anything."

Ellen dropped her eyes guiltily, thinking there probably hadn't been much of anything at all in Tina's pretty little head except pure self-interest. She found herself saying, without knowing she was going to, "I'm sorry, Ross."

He paused in his work and leaned on the handle of the ax, looking at her intensely. "For what?" he asked softly.

She made a futile gesture with her hand, not knowing how to answer, and Ross swung the ax back up into his hands again, but he paused before he went back to work. "There's no need to be," he said with wry honesty. "I'm not missing her."

He started splitting logs again then, and Ellen felt somehow uncomfortable as she wondered if he spoke the truth or was just covering up. "I'll go make some coffee," she volunteered, backing away from him.

"Sounds good," he replied laconically, not looking up as she turned on her heel to make her way back inside.

32

The coffee was perking by the time he came in with an armload of logs. He dumped them by the fireplace, then stacked them neatly in the holder provided, dusted his hands, and came into the kitchen as Ellen was getting out the cups and saucers.

"That smells good," he said appreciatively. "Are there any doughnuts or cookies?"

Ellen dug out a tin of chocolate chip cookies she'd made for the trip and placed it beside him on the counter, then poured him a cup of steaming hot black coffee.

"Delicious," he said around a mouthful of cookie. "Did Rosie make them?"

Ellen sighed inwardly, wondering if she was ever going to get used to his inability to concede her the smallest feminine talent. She was about to shrug without answering him one way or the other when Jake came yawning and stretching into the room.

"Ah, good . . . coffee!" he beamed, and Ellen handed him the cup she'd poured for herself. "And cookies!" he chortled, snatching up a handful to stuff into his mouth. "Ummm." He rolled his eyes heavenward in ecstasy. "Ellen's super-duper, double-chocolate, peanutty wonders!" He beamed at her affectionately. "You remembered!" he praised her.

"How could I help it?" she grimaced at him dryly. "You must have called me five times asking for them."

Jake looked hurt for a moment, his chubby cheeks pushing out as he pouted. "Well, I had to be sure," he complained like a little boy. "Rosie won't make them for me anymore. Says I'm getting fat." He gave Ellen and Ross a comical look of indignation as though he were highly insulted at his wife's accusation, though the truth of it rested bulgingly over his tight belt. "Besides," he sniffed, "she can't make them as good as you do anyway."

"It's her recipe, Jake," Ellen pointed out with affection.

33

"Yeah, but she doesn't do it right," he came back com-placently. "Give me another couple of 'em, Ross. You're hogging the whole damned batch!"

Ross shoved the tin over toward Jake, but his eyes were on Ellen, who let her own slide away from his without giving a sign that she was disgusted by the surprised speculation she saw on his face.

"Are the steaks thawed for tonight?" Jake then asked around the bite in his mouth. "I'm looking forward to some of that fresh meat you brought, old buddy." He grinned at Ross.

"Peg put them out this morning," Ellen reassured him, gesturing toward the counter.

The other members of the group began filtering into the room one by one then, and after everyone had had some coffee, Rosie suggested they take a drive around the area, as she was too tired to ski anymore that day.

Everyone agreed, and after they'd wrapped some potatoes in foil to slip into the oven for dinner, they all piled into the van again to take a leisurely tour of the area. When they got back, the men set up a barbecue stand and took over the job of grilling the steaks for dinner while the women put a salad together and set the table.

The dinner was delicious, the talk hilarious, and after the kitchen had been cleaned up, they filtered into the living room to light a fire in the fireplace, opened some wine, and sat down to talk some more. When the talk turned to politics, Ellen was surprised to find that she and Ross were in complete agreement on the issues of an up-coming election, the candidates they wanted to win, and their philosophy of government in general. She and John had been complete opposites on the subject, but their wrangling had always been good-natured and tolerant, so they had never had any problems to speak of.

She found Ross's eyes on her more than once, however,

as the discussion continued, and finally he brought up the qualities of their present governor, making it clear he didn't think much of the fellow.

"He's a perfect rat," Ellen agreed spontaneously. "I cancelled out John's vote for him at the last election, but it didn't help." She shook her head and chuckled. "John crowed over me for a week when that posturing hypocrite won, and he never once admitted the fool was a disaster as governor."

"John was always a softhearted idealist," Rosalynd put in, remembered fondness in her tone.

"Yes," Ellen agreed, her voice and eyes dreamy with love, "he was a darling." And then she blinked back her tears as she realized she was actually able to speak of him so naturally to her friends without hugging her hurt to herself.

Rosie smoothly changed the subject. "How about playing some poker?" she asked cheerfully. "I brought along the cards, and I feel lucky!"

Jake groaned. "I'm not playing at your table then," he asserted stoutly. "You beat me out of twenty dollars the last time you felt lucky, and the stakes were only a penny a pot!"

"Coward!" Rosie sniffed disdainfully. "You just don't know how to keep a poker face. I can read you like a book."

"So can I," Ellen laughed teasingly, "so you better not play at my table either, Jake."

Jake scowled at them both as he lit a huge black cigar in preparation for a night at the poker table. As it turned out, Ellen ended up at a table with Ross, Rosie, and Randy, whereupon she immediately protested she was being drowned in alliteration, while Jake, Peg, Bill, and Marie played at another table.

As they seated themselves, Rosie whispered in a loud

tone that Ellen had better watch Ross like a hawk because he cheated like a riverboat gambler, and Ellen replied with a snort that she was no mean hand at palming an ace or two herself! Ross lit a thin cheroot and his blue eyes gleamed at the two of them over his cupped hands like a laser beam. "Character assassination won't win you a game this time, Rosie," he crowed dangerously, "and neither will cheating," he added as he switched his stern gaze to Ellen. She smiled sweetly at him and sat down very demurely, batting her eyes at him with beguiling innocence as she muttered, "We'll see."

The game turned out to be hilarious, with Ross and Ellen openly vying with each other to see who could cheat more blatantly, while Rosie and Randy formed an alliance that resulted in one or the other of them winning every hand. When Ross and Ellen caught on to the other couple's strategy, their mutual outrage was loud and vociferous until, with a great deal of waggling eyebrows and nonverbal strategizing, the two of them ganged up on their erstwhile rivals to the point where they were passing cards to each other underneath the table.

The game came to an end when they got caught because a card Ross thought he was passing to Ellen somehow ended up in Rosie's hand instead, and amidst a lot of good-natured wrangling and outrageous accusations, everyone decided no one could be trusted, and therefore they'd better break out the backgammon board instead. That didn't last long either, however, as no one wanted to sit by quietly without kibitzing, and, finally, Rosie gave a huge yawn and informed everyone she couldn't stand another moment of *their* unprincipled behavior.

Since Ellen hadn't had a nap like the others that afternoon, she was beginning to have an attack of the yawns, so she elected to go to bed as well.

"It's my turn to make breakfast in the morning," Marie

called out, and Ellen gave her a grateful smile over her shoulder as she left the room, but she didn't get away before she caught Ross's eyes on her once again, with the enigmatic expression in them she had seen there more than once and which had begun to puzzle and, more to the point, alarm her unreasonably, though why it should, she couldn't have said.

Defiantly, she donned the pink fuzzy pajamas again, though her last thought before she snuggled down under the covers and closed her eyes to sleep was that she wished Ross Sayer could see her in that black number John had bought her the last time he'd gone to Kansas City. She bet *that* little baby would change his mind in a hurry about her lack of femininity!

CHAPTER FOUR

Despite her best intentions, Ellen somehow found herself skiing with Ross again the next morning. She told herself it was only natural since they were the two best skiers of the bunch and tended to leave everyone else behind, but what really bothered her was that she was enjoying it so much! It was downright disconcerting to have to revise some of her prejudices about Ross Sayer now that he seemed to be making every effort to help her have a good time, and she even had to begin cautioning herself not to fall too much under his spell since she knew she was definitely not his type.

She was helped along in that effort when, after an hour or so, the beautiful little black-haired doll who had been flirting with him at the lodge the day before appeared out of nowhere and breathlessly asked him to help her with one of her skis, which had developed a tendency to come loose.

Ellen watched with a sardonic eye for a while as the two of them played a mean game of flirtation then with an inner snort she decided she'd had enough of playing audience to the woman's gushing little exclamations about how clever and strong Ross was, and Ross's sexy brand of eye contact with his admirer. It took a few minutes to get his attention, but at last she was able to tell him she was going on ahead, her expression making it clear she didn't

38

enjoy playing gooseberry to their mutual admiration society.

Ross nodded rather curtly, it seemed to Ellen, and she took off without a backward glance, feeling both irritated and grateful that she had been reminded of what sort of woman did appeal to him.

She skied by herself for a while, still enjoying the glorious scenery and weather and the sheer release of physical activity, but her enthusiasm was slightly dampened, and she found herself missing John's company more so than she had the day before. He had been a good skier, too, and they had enjoyed these yearly trips enormously.

Perhaps to get her mind off her loneliness, she picked a particularly difficult slope to descend before calling it a morning, the moguls coming at her like miniature mountains ready to trip her up at the slightest error. And, of course, she made a bad one, and went jouncing down the slope on her bottom for a short distance before she did a complete flipflop and ended up winded on her stomach.

She had to lie there for several moments until she could get her breath back and begin to assess her damages. She could tell she hadn't broken anything, but she had the feeling she was going to be black and blue for quite a while after this little tumble, and she felt like a fool to boot, since she had somehow managed to do exactly the wrong thing at exactly the wrong time when she had known she was making a mistake even as she made it.

She was about to push herself up on her elbows when she heard the swish of skis near her and felt a wet spray of snow in her face as the skier came to a stop beside her. "Are you all right?" Ross's voice was positively grim as he snapped off his skis, then squatted down beside her to place a hand on the middle of her back.

She nodded her head, still a little short of breath, and felt him begin an examination of her body that was disturbingly thorough. "I'm fine!" she yelped as his hand came up her thigh toward her bottom, and she made the effort to push herself over onto her back to glare up at him.

"You damned little fool!" he hissed at her angrily, his jaw set and grim. "You were taking this slope too fast and you know it!"

"I was not!" she snapped back at him, pushing her lower lip out stubbornly. "I just . . ." She started to tell him what she'd done wrong, but he was in no mood to listen.

"Hell, no," he snarled sarcastically. "Miss Athlete of the Year couldn't possibly admit she was wrong about anything, could she? What are you really trying to do, Ellen? Kill yourself so you can be with John again?"

Infuriated, Ellen reacted without thought, swinging her fist at him with every intention of knocking his block off right there on the spot! He caught her wrist in an ironhard grip, his face as hard as stone, and in a movement so fast it seemed like a blur to Ellen, he was down beside her, pinning her arms to the ground while he dipped his head and pressed his lips against hers with a fierceness that she was certain was going to give her a fat lip along with all the other bruises she was going to carry around for days!

She struggled under that onslaught, trying desperately to escape the pain he was inflicting, until at last he seemed to become aware of what he was doing and lessened the pressure of his mouth. He didn't stop kissing her, however, but shifted his weight until he was fully atop her, grinding her body down into the snow!

Ellen was gasping for breath by the time he raised his head and stared down at her, his ice blue eyes clear and cold as he studied her without expression for a moment. Ellen blinked up at him, shock and vulnerability making her mouth tremble. Ross shifted his gaze to her mouth, muttered something unintelligible, then lowered his head

40

again to stroke and soothe the tremble away with his cool, gentle lips.

Ellen shivered, tensed, then relaxed under him as his onslaught changed from rough savagery to artful seduction, which turned out to be far more dangerous to Ellen's peace of mind than his anger had been. She had never been kissed by a man with a mustache before Ross had done so, and again she found it imparted an intimate, teasing sensation that was so erotically delicious, she lost all track of everything but what it was doing to her. Her mouth opened under his voluntarily this time, and Ross's tongue slid inside without an instant's hesitation to be met by her own in a mutual tasting that ignited a fire of need in both of them.

Ross released her arms; she circled his neck with them, and their bodies began a writhing effort to get closer that had the two of them gasping for breath and straining for each other within seconds. If a nearby skier hadn't given a hooting shout of encouragement to their efforts, Ellen didn't know what would have happened right there beneath God's blue sky and in full sight of anyone who wanted to watch!

Ross raised his head in reaction to that shout, his eyes cloudy now with the passion the two of them had incited in each other, lifted himself onto his elbows, and growled down at her, "Damn it, I told you what would happen if you challenged me again!" then flung himself off her to get to his feet.

Feeling bruised, battered, and utterly wrung out, both physically and emotionally, Ellen snarled at him in her turn. "Well, if you didn't regard every damned thing I do as a challenge, it wouldn't have!"

He glared down at her. "Throwing a punch at me isn't a challenge?" he snapped nastily. "Pardon me! I must have all the wrong instincts!"

41

"You certainly do!" Ellen blustered, forcing herself into a sitting position, then wincing and giving a heartfelt groan as she felt the expected bruises begin their demand for her attention.

"Are you hurt?" Ross asked in a tone of voice that might have been used to ask if she was a traitor to her country.

Ellen opened the eyes she had closed in reaction to her pain and scorched him with a look. "*Hell, no!*" she said with slow, distinct, scathing sarcasm. "I'm in tiptop shape, buster! I just like to play the suffering female because I know it appeals to your male ego!"

Ross pulled off one of his gloves and extended a hand down to her. "Then play it all the way, why don't you, and let me help you up!"

Ellen would have swatted the hand away if she thought she could have gotten up without it, but she was not at all certain she could, so she grabbed it, felt him grip her forearm and lift her like a piece of cotton candy out of the snow. Then she fell into his arms as her legs gave out under her.

"You *are* hurt!" he said angrily as he wrapped his arms around her to support her.

"No, I'm not," she insisted. "I'm just a little weak in the knees. Give me a second to get my balance and I'll be all right!"

She felt Ross give an impatient grunt, but he didn't say anything more for the few minutes she remained locked in his arms until she felt strong enough to stand on her own. He held her elbows and watched her suspiciously until he was certain she really had recovered, then slowly dropped his hands.

"Did you see my other ski?" Ellen muttered, searching the area for the article with her eyes.

"It's back up the hill a few yards," Ross clipped out.

42

"I'll get it for you." He kept turning his head backward to watch her as he made his way up the hill to retrieve her ski, and Ellen, who was in no mood for any more of his scorching glares, finally turned her back on him and began to feel herself to make sure she really was all right. Satisfied that she was, she was just turning back as he rejoined her, her missing ski in his hand.

"We'll walk down," he informed her coldly.

"We'll ski down," she informed *him* equally coldly.

His look was one of total exasperation for a moment before he threw down the ski and bent to get his own. Ellen retrieved the ski, found her other one nearby, and fastened them to her boots.

"I'll follow you," Ross said.

"Fine," Ellen replied, and started off slowly down the hill, feeling every aching cell in her body with excruciating clarity, but determined she wasn't even going to so much as wince, though Ross was behind her and couldn't see her face.

They made it to the bottom without further incident, but when Ellen had taken off her skis to walk to the lodge, she was limping visibly, and Ross circled her waist with his arm, merely tightening his hold when she glowered up at him and made to pull away.

"Don't be any more of a damned fool than you already have been," Ross said, his voice now wearily impatient.

Ellen faced forward, swallowed down an enormous desire to cry, and remained silent. When they got to the lodge, Ross seated her at a table and went to get them both cups of hot coffee. When he came back to the table, Ellen was sitting with her chin propped on her hands, her mouth pouting like a child's, and her eyes glittering brightly with unshed tears.

Ross placed her coffee before her, then seated himself and took a deep swallow of his own coffee before he put it down to stare at her enigmatically. "So you can cry," he said in a low, interested voice. "I was beginning to wonder."

Ellen's eyes flashed fire at him, then she dropped her gaze and lifted her coffee to her lips to sip gratefully at the hot, strong beverage.

"You're about the most exasperating woman I've ever met, do you know that, Ellen?" he said then with a wry quirk of his lips under the luxurious mustache. "I honestly don't know what to make of you."

Ellen glanced at him, one eyebrow raised sardonically. "You don't have to make anything at all of me, Ross," she said dryly. "I've known from the first day we met that you didn't think I was good enough for John. I didn't meet your standards for . . . ah . . . beauty, for femininity, or for much of anything else, I gather." She shrugged unconcernedly, though inside, for the very first time, it became clear to her just why, aside from the obvious, she had always felt such antagonism toward Ross. He had pricked her own inner feelings of inadequacy because she wasn't beautiful in the Madison Avenue sense. Her face was quite ordinary aside from the lovely clarity of her clear, hazel eyes and exquisite curve of her generous mouth. She was too slender, without the soft curves of a more voluptuous woman, and she considered the soft brown of her hair mousy and unspectacular.

Ross was frowning at her now and she smiled back at him, the smile an echo of her thoughts. She had overheard his ill-advised remark about John marrying her for her money when she was younger and a lot less certain of her own attributes. Since living with John, she had come to appreciate herself much more, a result of his own unstinting appreciation of her . . . as a woman, as a wife, as a friend and companion, and as a person in her own right. The antagonism for Ross hadn't abated in those few short

44

years she had had with John because she hadn't let it. It had become a habit, and in their mutual avoidance of each other, there had been no chance for either of them to really get to know the other.

"And just how did you come to get to know so much about how I regarded you?" Ross asked now, his face closed and unrevealing and slightly intimidating.

Deciding to get the past out in the open once and for all and be done with it, Ellen answered him honestly, a slight smile tugging at her lovely mouth. "I overheard you telling Rosie and Jake how disappointed you were that John had married for money," she said, her tone matter of fact. "I knew it wasn't true, of course. John proposed to me before I ever got that inheritance, and it knocked both of us for a loop. But I was young and uncertain and much too vulnerable for my own good to what others thought of me." She met Ross's eyes squarely as she finished her speech. "Therefore, I didn't like you very much at all from that point on, Ross Sayer. I'm not sure I do now, but at least if it turns out I don't, it will be for better reasons than it was in the past."

Ross studied her for a long moment, and Ellen was unable to tell what he was thinking. She felt so much better for having gained a little insight into her own emotions, however, that she didn't much care. She felt light and easy, as though a burden had been lifted from her shoulders.

When Ross finally spoke, it was without apology. "You weren't what I expected, it's true," he said levelly. "John had always dated the class beauties in high school and his first two years of college, anyway, and after that we weren't as close, since I transferred to an agricultural school. When John brought you home, you were a different type of woman altogether from the ones I'd always associated with him." He paused then, his voice dropping

45

lower and taking on a note of firmness that was gratifyingly convincing. "I did consider you rather unspectacular, as a matter of fact, but that was before I got to know you, both personally and from the things John told me about you. Since then I've come to realize you have a beauty all your own, Ellen. It isn't obvious and it isn't typical, but it's very real nonetheless."

Ellen barely had time to absorb his compliment before he went on, and this time his sincerity wasn't so welcome. "But your attitude toward me has always made it very hard for me to like you, Ellen. I could sense your anger every time I came near you, and since I didn't know the reason for it, I simply reacted by returning your hostility. And you're right about my considering you unfeminine as well. Until you cuddled up to me in the van the other night, I confess I had a hard time understanding why John was so damned much in love with you. It seemed to me you'd be about as warm and loving in a man's bed as"—he hesitated before giving her another of his wry smiles before he finished what he'd been about to say with devastating honesty—"as another man," he concluded quietly.

Ellen looked at him wide-eyed, stunned by his opinion, hurt by it, and then enraged by it! She opened her mouth to express that rage when he reached across to take her hand in his own, shaking his head with rueful patience.

"Let's not start up again, Ellen," he said quietly. "I've changed my mind. You ought to know that from what just happened up on the hill if the incident in the van didn't convince you." He leaned back to scan her body with his devastatingly expressive blue eyes, and one eyebrow arched humorously. "There's a power of sexuality in that slender body of yours, lady. You reduce a man to the raw essentials faster than any woman I've ever made love to, and if you weren't the widow of one of my best friends, I'd have you stripped and in my bed so fast you wouldn't

46

know what hit you, and I suspect I wouldn't let you out of it for a week."

Swallowing, Ellen forced herself to hold his gaze, unable to deny that if he wanted to, he could make every one of his words come true. He had a power of sexuality of his own that called to hers, and she knew with utter certainty that the two of them would be very, very good in bed together. She took refuge from that knowledge, and from the equal certainty that their mutual physical attraction was just that—entirely physical—by pointing out the obvious.

"Then I guess it's a good thing I am the widow of your best friend, Ross, because I'm not interested in an affair with you or with anyone else. I'm too used to being made love to to settle for just having sex."

Ross nodded, his eyes narrow and contemplative. "I'm aware of that," he said levelly. "That's why I've been trying damned hard to keep my hands off you. I haven't been doing a very good job of it because I haven't been involved with a woman since Tina left, and because you have a disconcerting habit of taking me off guard," he added dryly, smiling as Ellen bristled a little, then settled down to accept his viewpoint.

"All right," she said on a deep breath. "I'll, ah, try to see that that doesn't happen anymore. We don't see much of each other anyway, and since I'm very far from being your type, when we're not thrown together like this, our . . . uh . . . temporary aberration should die a natural death." She knew her cheeks were burning for some reason, and Ross's interested, amused survey of them only increased their heat.

He didn't reply to her solution to their mutual problem directly, but rather asked, in a lazy, curious fashion, "What do you consider my type, Ellen?"

She looked at him in surprise, then shrugged as though

the answer were obvious. "Why, women like Tina, of course. Helpless, beautiful, brainless, and crawling with femininity."

She flushed even more then, both at her overly honest description of his ex-wife and because he had obviously perceived by her tone that she considered none of those qualities truly descriptive of femininity. He asked the obvious question.

"What do *you* consider feminine, Ellen?"

She looked down at where her hands were fiddling uncomfortably with her coffee cup, then raised her eyes again to face him unflinchingly. "I think I'm about as close to real femininity as you're ever likely to come, Ross. At least John thought so, and he's the one who taught me what being a woman's really all about."

There was a short, electric silence between them, then Ellen got to her feet, tired suddenly of defending herself before this man whom she was sure would never agree with either John's or her own description of what constituted a feminine woman. "I'm going out to the van, Ross," she said wearily. "The others should be back soon, and I don't feel like skiing anymore just now." Which was as close as she was prepared to come to admitting that she was one aching mass of bruised flesh. "When Jake gets here, would you ask him to run me to the condominium if the rest of the bunch isn't ready to return yet? I need a hot bath and a nap."

He got to his feet as well and took her arm in his hand. "I'll run you back, Ellen," he said quietly. "I have a spare key to the van."

She sighed, needing some peace from the company of this exasperating man, but unwilling to refuse his offer and perhaps start up another fight between them. They were both silent on the walk to the van and on the drive to the condominium, and when they arrived, Ellen reached for

48

the door handle, grateful that she was going to be allowed the place to herself for a while in order to take a hot, healing, leisurely bath and then climb between her sheets for some much needed, recuperative sleep. She was startled, therefore, when Ross climbed out his side of the van.

"You don't need to stay with me," Ellen hastened to reassure him. "I'll be all right."

He looked her up and down, but he didn't pause or return to the van. "You need a good massage with some strong liniment," he said in a tone she knew was useless to challenge. She did anyway, however, exasperated beyond maintaining control.

"Ross, that would be a very dumb thing to do, considering what we've just been talking about, don't you think?" she asked, tight-lipped.

"Why?" he came back at her lazily. "I like my women dumb, beautiful, and willing, remember? Do any of those descriptions fit you?"

"I have my own brand of beauty," she reminded him scathingly, more hurt than she would have credited at hearing him more or less admit that his so convincing description of her earlier had been just a lot of words.

"I know," he said with a dangerous smile. "But we've already established that your brand is not what appeals to me, haven't we? I should be able to control myself under the circumstances."

Ellen turned on her heel, her back stiff and unyielding, her fists clenched, her jaw tight as she preceded him into the condominium. She went straight to her room to gather up some clean underclothing, then disappeared into the bathroom to turn on the taps and let the tub fill with the hottest water she could stand. She stripped off her clothes, willing her mind to blankness, refusing to let her seething thoughts surface to a point where they could hurt her.

49

She soaked and soaked and soaked, letting the hot water ease out some of the aches and pains she suffered until she was almost asleep before Ross knocked at the door.

"Have you drowned?" he called in to her. "You've been in there long enough to. Come on out and get yourself doctored. Just wrap yourself up in a towel."

Ellen's eyes came open to stare wearily at the wall in front of her before she sat up and let the water out, then stood up and dried off. She was in a state of numbness where the thought of appearing before Ross in the scanty protection of a towel and letting him handle her in the intimacy of a massage didn't even faze her. She had taken his words about her not appealing to him absolutely literally.

He was waiting in the hall outside the bathroom when she came out, her panties in her hand, and his eyes were cool and remote as he gestured her to enter her bedroom. She did so, stretched out on the bed, and closed her eyes to await the expected massage. She frowned slightly when he tugged the towel from around her and spread it over her hips, then relaxed as she felt the warm heat of some lotion being poured over her back, thinking it was thoughtful of him to warm the stuff instead of pouring it ice cold on her skin.

Then his hands were on her, smearing the liquid into her muscles, their warm strength gentle, comforting, and terribly soothing. She was half-dozing when she felt the towel being lifted away from her, then felt the liquid being poured on her buttocks. Her eyes came open, a wary look in them, but Ross chose that moment to inform her in a low-voiced, rumbling, bland tone, that she had a beauty of a bruise on her butt.

"I landed on it pretty hard," she mumbled drowsily.

"I know. I saw you fall," he replied quietly. "You scared the hell out of me."

Ellen's intended reply died in her throat when she felt his hands on her there, their kneading, gentle touch tingling her skin with arousal. "That . . . that's enough, Ross," she said in a nervous quaver. "It . . . ah . . . hurts too much."

"Does it?" he asked, his voice dropping into a lower, sexier register. "Then turn over and I'll do your front."

"I can do my front!" she said quickly, alarm in her voice.

"Sure you can," he said with lazy, aroused amusement. "But I can do it better."

"Ross . . ." she started on a strangled note, only to have her words choked off as he flipped her over onto her back. He was looking down at her with his beautiful eyes half closed, his jaw tensed, but it was the fact that he was obviously, gloriously, aroused that caught her attention. She stared at that bulging maleness with alarmed fascination, then darted her eyes up to his face to see him smiling down at her grimly.

"Oh, yes," he said with soft, dangerous huskiness in his tone. "I want you like hell. You should never trust a man who says he doesn't want you when he's just half-raped you in the snow before anyone who cared to look."

She drew back against the bed as though she wanted to escape that total, male concentration he was giving her nude body, but Ross leaned forward to place his powerful arms on either side of her.

"If you lie very still, Ellen, and don't provoke me in any way," he said, still in that soft, dangerous voice, "I may let you get away with a few kisses and a little harmless exploration. Or would you rather challenge me again, here in this bedroom, without a thing to distract us, and see if I can stop myself from giving you exactly what you're beginning to want already?"

Ellen swallowed, gulped down a protest she was afraid

would provoke him to do exactly what he promised, and silently cursed her breasts for betraying to him the message he had picked up on with unerring quickness. It was more than she could do to agree to what he proposed, but he took her silence as assent and lowered his head to tease her mouth with his tongue until her lips came open to receive it more fully.

At that, he gave a muffled groan and moved to stretch himself out half over her, cupping her head with his hands as he began to plunder her mouth with lips and tongue and teeth until he had Ellen shaking beneath him and returning his erotic loveplay with her own mouth uninhibitedly, though she managed to keep her hands rigid against their insane desire to grip his hips and pull him more fully atop her.

"Do it," he breathed into her mouth as he felt her hands twitching restlessly beside him. "Hold me if you want to. Touch me. You do want to, don't you, baby." It was a statement, not a question, and an entirely accurate one, and as he shifted himself more fully onto her, Ellen's hands came up of their own accord to grip his hips and press him into her.

She felt his heated maleness pressing against her like a welcome brand, and wanted that heat inside her like a person dying of thirst wants water. She moved beneath him, her hips beginning an automatic, thrusting rhythm that brought a shudder to his large, heavy frame as he pushed back against her and opened his mouth wider over hers to begin a duplicate motion with his tongue.

Ellen was suddenly, devastatingly, out of control in reaction to that irresistible combination, and she went a little wild, opening her legs to him, encircling him with her arms, devouring his mouth with her own. Ross went over the edge then himself, and his movements were savage with his need as he thrust a hand between them to free his clothing and release the surging, dominant life that Ellen wanted so badly she was whimpering with her own need.

Her body leapt to his when he entered her, opening joyously to him and struggling to draw from him the very essence of the maleness that called to her own femininity so strongly she felt it in the deepest layer of her being. There was no question of holding back anything of what she had to give, nor of denying that she wanted just as much from him.

It was a coupling that rocked them both to their very souls, a wild, joyous, completely uninhibited joining of two people who had been denied such passion far too long and who had unexpectedly found in each other a primal compatibility neither had experienced quite so vividly ever before. And when it was over, Ross's incredulous "God! Oh, my God, Ellen!" echoed in her ears with a ringing vitality she was to remember both awake and in her dreams for a long time to come.

CHAPTER FIVE

Their euphoria lasted only a few minutes before it was replaced by a mutual wariness. Ellen's relaxed, natural contentedness in the aftermath of her passion gradually changed to a feeling of disorientation, confusion, and bewilderment. She felt off-balance, as though something in her well-ordered universe had shifted out of kilter.

"You . . . ah . . . you'd better go back and get the others," she faltered weakly, needing desperately some time alone to find her feet emotionally again.

Ross lifted himself from her to turn over on his back, raking a hand through his thick hair as he lay with his eyes closed for a few seconds. "Yes," he said finally, flatly. "Give me a minute."

They lay in silence side by side for a while, each locked in their own thoughts, before a shiver chased Ellen's skin in reaction to the coolness of the room. The movement seemed to break the spell of lassitude gripping Ross. He gave a deep sigh, moved his hands to arrange himself in his clothes, and pulled his jeans zipper closed before sitting up on the side of the bed.

"You'd better climb under the covers," he said in a remote tone. "You're cold."

Ellen nodded, though he couldn't see it, and when at last he got to his feet, she did as he suggested, her body seized with a fit of trembling that sprang from both physical and emotional causes. She watched as Ross paced to the door, his back straight and masculine, then called his name as a sudden thought seized her, filling her with a nameless anxiety.

"Ross!" And as he turned to look at her, his expression closed and tired, she voiced her fear. "You won't . . . won't come to my room tonight, will you?" she asked in a low, husky voice filled with her anxiety. "Please . . . I don't . . . I'm not . . ."

His face tightened for an instant, then relaxed as he ran a hand through his hair again and came back to stand at the foot of the bed looking down at her, his hands on his hips. "No," he said with quiet gentleness. "I plan to stay out of your way entirely for the rest of the trip."

Ellen relaxed, her eyes wide and showing her gratitude for his understanding. "Thank you," she said with gentle dignity.

He nodded, the corner of his mouth under his mustache quirking with something indefinable for an instant before he turned away again. "Rest for a while, Ellen," he suggested over his shoulder. "I'll tell the others about your fall and they'll leave you alone."

"I will," she agreed quietly. And when the door closed behind him, she did just that, letting the taut, tense muscles of her body relax one by one as she contemplated what had just happened and tried to make sense of it. Gradually, her mind began to cope with her need for a logical explanation, and she faced the fact that her loneliness, her long-denied sensual nature, and Ross's overwhelming masculinity had all combined to lead her to this moment. She finally realized it was necessary to just accept what had happened and go easy on herself for behaving like a normal human being instead of a saint.

But facing and accepting her own human nature didn't erase the sense of lonely need for two strong arms around

55

her and murmured love sounds to ease her through the empty aftermath of passion, experiences John had always given her . . . experiences two people in love shared as they comforted each other and expressed their love after their bodies had been satisfied.

And it was that need that would have convinced her an affair with Ross would prove to be a mistake, even if he hadn't already said the same thing. She needed a lot more than an explosive physical relationship to make her feel complete. She needed the concern and care and commitment she'd had with John, and wanted again with someone . . . somewhere . . . sometime. For all she knew, Ross probably wanted the same thing, but it was clear he couldn't find it with her, and since that was true, she didn't even acknowledge the deep-seated sad regret that rested somewhere in her subconscious.

She fell asleep then and didn't wake again until Rosie came into her room to ask if she felt well enough to get up for dinner.

"Sure," she smiled easily at her friend, sitting up and giving a long stretch that made the covers slip down and reveal the fact that she was nude.

Rosie's eyes widened with interested speculation. "What happened to the bunny costume?" she asked humorously.

Ellen was glad the shadows in the room concealed her sudden flush. "I was too tired and beat up to fiddle with it," she replied offhandedly. "Give me a few minutes to get dressed, Rosie, and I'll be out. What are we having tonight anyway?" she chattered, diverting the other woman successfully.

"Hamburgers," Rosie grimaced. "Everyone's too tired to go to any trouble."

"Sounds good to me," Ellen said, keeping her tone casual.

"Okay, then," Rosie agreed as she crossed to the door. "See you in a few minutes."

Ellen dressed slowly in dark brown slacks and a white turtleneck sweater, gathering her resources for the forthcoming meeting with Ross. She brushed her hair, then left it loose, somehow feeling she might need its concealing drape on this particular evening, then applied some light green eyeshadow and a pale gloss to her lips, which were becoming slightly chapped from the cold and wind.

Taking a deep breath, she left her room, walking slowly to accommodate her still aching muscles and bruises, though she was gratified to note her limp was gone, and entered the living room to find with a resigned sense of inevitability that Ross was its only occupant. He was stretched out on the sofa, a glass of wine in his hand, his eyes closed and his face tiredly peaceful.

Ellen would have made her way to the kitchen without disturbing him, but his blue eyes came open to fix her to the spot where she stood gazing down at him, her eyes wary. "Feeling better?" he asked without a trace of intimacy in his tone. He sounded merely friendly and casually concerned for her physical well-being.

She nodded, her throat closing up for a moment before she could react to his lead and keep the conversation on an easy level. "My limp's gone," she said in a tone to match his. "I'm still sore, but that will pass."

He sat up, and his smile was easy and friendly as he looked up at her. "Yeah, but I wouldn't want to be you on the slopes tomorrow," he teased her casually. "You're going to have to work to call it fun for a few hours."

Feeling much better suddenly as a result of his attitude, Ellen smiled back at him ruefully. "You said it," she agreed wryly.

"Want some wine?" he invited, getting to his feet to pour it for her from the carafe on the coffee table.

"Yes, thanks." Ellen moved closer to take it from him. "Maybe it will lubricate my muscles."

One of the others joined them then, and for the rest of the evening, and for the rest of the trip, Ellen and Ross managed to keep their contact easy and casual, without alerting anyone to the fact that they had shared one of the most intimate acts possible between a man and a woman.

On the last night before they were to leave they all went out to a club for some drinking and dancing, and no one seemed to notice that only Ross and Ellen never shared a dance. Perhaps it was because some of the single men at the club, upon discovering that she was unattached, began to beat a path to her table, and she accepted their attentions with an easy, self-confident casualness that made them keep their place even when their eyes shone with admiration for her face and figure and relaxed, comfortable sense of humor and intelligent conversation.

Ellen found Ross's eyes on her only once that night. She was dancing with a young man who was something of a cutup, and as she laughed up at him after one of his jokes she happened to turn her head to the chair where Ross sat with his legs stretched out, a glass of beer in his hand, and his blue eyes fixed on her with a rather stony, enigmatic gaze that confused and bothered her. But then the young man claimed her attention again, and she had to turn away, only then realizing that Ross himself was not dancing at all that evening, though there were quite a few looks of invitation directed his way from time to time, all of which he seemed impervious to.

On the trip home the next day, both of them somehow made certain they wouldn't be seated together again, but when Ellen pulled into her own driveway after getting her yellow Corvette from Rosie and Jake's, she was not surprised when Ross's blue pickup truck pulled up behind her.

He came to her side as she climbed out of her car and said, "We need to talk," then held out his hand for her trunk key so that he could carry her bag in for her.

She nodded, gave him the key, then went to open her front door. She was turning up the heat when he entered the house and set her bag down in the hallway. "Do you want something to drink?" she asked quietly.

He shook his head no. "I need to get to the ranch," he said equally quietly. So Ellen made a movement of her hand to gesture him into the bright, cheerful living room, and followed him to settle herself upon the gaily patterned couch.

He didn't sit down, but paced in front of her for a moment, pausing to look at a portrait of John on one wall, then finally turning to look down at her. "I'm sorry about what happened, Ellen," he said, tight-lipped. "I sure as hell didn't plan it."

Ellen looked down at her lap, studying her hands. "There's no need to be sorry, Ross," she said with calm quietness. "I didn't plan it either. I think you were right when you said we were both . . . hungry." She looked up at him them, giving a deep sigh. "It just happened, Ross. I was as much responsible as you were. Neither of us needs to rake ourselves over the coals about it. We're only human."

He shrugged, giving a short laugh. "We are that, all right," he commented dryly. Then he looked at her again, his blue eyes clear and cool. "I just wanted you to know I'm not going to follow up on it. Tina burned my bridges pretty thoroughly as far as marriage is concerned, and you're not a woman to settle for anything less."

She looked back at him, her gaze clear and direct. "No," she agreed with him softly. "I'm not."

He flexed his shoulder muscles in a tired movement, then started to leave, but paused in front of her, his eyes roaming her face thoroughly and settling on her mouth. "Do you mind my telling you that I wish to God you could?" he asked very softly with a husky undertone of desire in his voice. "Or that you weren't John's widow so that I could seduce you again . . . and again . . . with a clear conscience?"

A slow sweet smile of sadness curved Ellen's lovely mouth. "No, I don't mind at all, Ross," she said with grave solemnity. "I'm glad to know you thought it was as good as I did."

"It was more than good, Ellen," Ross said in deep tones of sincerity. "It was almost too much more to let me walk out of here without having it again. But it wouldn't stop there, would it?"

Ellen bit her lip against the tide of desire that was coursing through her body, making her feel flushed with heat, making her want to stop Ross from walking out at all. "No," she breathed quickly, forcing the word through her lips. "It wouldn't stop there, and that's not what either of us wants."

His arrested stillness brought her eyes up to his. "Isn't it?" he said with soft thoughtfulness. "I wonder . . ." But then he shook off the spell they were beginning to weave between them and crossed to the door.

"Be happy, Ellen," he spoke curtly without turning to look at her.

"I'll try, Ross," she answered so softly she was certain he didn't hear. And then she listened as the door closed behind him, closed her eyes against the desire to call him back, and jumped up to begin using some sort of mundane physical activity to blot out the shaking, almost overwhelming need to use her body in another way.

CHAPTER SIX

Ellen didn't see Ross again until Memorial Day. Meanwhile, she had begun to turn her life around in those few short months, finding a good manager for the bookstore, so that she was able to spend less and less time working there herself, seeing more of her other friends, much to Rosie's delight, and finally even beginning to date.

The problem with dating in a mid-sized town, however, was that there were so few single males available, and those who were seemed to invariably develop an annoying tendency to want to go much too fast, much too soon. Ellen wasn't sure whether it was her money, her personality, or some innate sex appeal she must have developed since her previous dating days, but she soon began to tire of the inevitable wrestling matches, the wearisome process of breaking off a relationship that had barely begun, and the blurted-out proposals that always managed to catch her by surprise, perhaps because they always came much too soon to be based on real love.

Consequently, she soon began casting around for something more satisfying to do with her life than provide a target for every sex-starved male within a twenty-mile radius who must also think it quite handy of her to have a house and a business and a healthy bank account.

Purely as a temporary measure, she started working as a volunteer for the gubernatorial candidate she favored who would be challenging the incumbent the following November. This entailed a couple of weekly trips to Topeka, where she soon began to meet, and date, a much more patient variety of male than she had heretofore encountered. They might not have been ultimately any less predatory than those she met at home, but they were certainly more sophisticated about stalking their prey, which gave her the opportunity to experience some pleasantly companionable, interesting evenings before the line had to be drawn once again, at which point they generally disappeared from the scene altogether.

One of them had just done so the preceding evening when Ross's call came, taking Ellen completely by surprise, and interrupting a bout of spring cleaning she was using to dispel a fit of the glooms that had descended upon her at the unsatisfactory thought that this sort of thing might go on indefinitely.

"Hello?" She answered the phone, then promptly sneezed as a mite of dust from the cloth she carried entered her nose.

"Do you have a cold?" Ross asked in the low-timbered, seductive tones that still haunted her dreams occasionally.

"Ah . . . er . . . no," Ellen answered, noting that her heartbeat was accelerating alarmingly and her palms were suddenly moist. "Ross? Is that you?"

"It's me," he replied in an easy tone that nevertheless held a hint of wryness. "How are you, Ellen?"

"Oh . . . er . . . fine, just fine," Ellen stammered, feeling like a schoolgirl being called for her first date. She grimaced at hearing herself and had a sudden urge to stamp her foot in exasperation at her own silliness.

"How about you, Ross? Are you okay?" She managed to sound slightly more adult.

"Nothing's changed with me," he answered laconically, causing her to wonder if he meant he still wanted her, or if he was talking about still being averse to marriage, or both, or just that he was simply all right. Ellen wasn't sure what she wanted the truth to be . . . all she was really sure of was that the mere sound of Ross's voice had the power to waken all her senses to a degree not one of the men she'd dated over the past few months had even approached. She was also sure, as the silence between them drew out, that she was going to go crazy with the suspense if Ross didn't tell her soon why he had called.

"Ah . . . er . . . how's the cattle market?" she asked inanely, just to break the silence that was threatening to break her nerves.

"Fine," he answered in an amused tone. "How's the book market?"

"Fine," she answered, then felt like a fool. "Ross," she said impatiently, "you must know I'm dying of curiosity to know why you've called. Why did you?"

He chuckled. "Still my blunt, straight-to-the-point little firecracker, aren't you, honey?" he drawled, but there was affection beneath his amusement, so Ellen found it hard to take offense.

"Nothing's changed with me either," she said firmly, though she wondered if that was strictly true, as she had the distinct feeling that if Ross were with her this moment instead of calling her on the telephone, she would fly into his arms for the first honest, gratifying sensation she'd had for far too long.

"Hasn't it?" he said quietly. "That's not what I hear."

"What do you mean?" she asked, puzzled by his words.

"Never mind," he said offhandedly. "I called to invite you to a picnic, Ellen. The gang's coming out next Saturday for a ground picnic by the river. Would you like to come?"

Would I! was her instantaneous mental response, but her verbal one was much more cautious. "You mean Rosie and Jake and everybody?" she asked, stalling for time, but knowing in her heart what her answer was going to be.

"Plus the kids," Ross answered lazily. "Of course, you have to pay your way."

Ellen's heart speeded up alarmingly at his words, and she had the disconcerting impression he had meant for her to take his words other than as he really meant them.

"You have to bring part of the food," he relented after Ellen's silence had gone on just a second too long. "Rosie's organizing it. If you want to come, why don't you call her and see what she wants you to bring."

"All . . . all right," she heard her own voice accepting before she had known she was going to. But once having committed herself, she found an eager anticipation growing inside her that she knew she was a fool for experiencing. "I'll look forward to it, Ross," she added, then almost moaned aloud her despair at the note of husky invitation she had allowed to creep into her voice.

"So will I, Ellen," Ross replied in an approximation of her tone that brought goose bumps to her skin. "See you then, all right?"

"Yes, Ross . . . see you then," she managed more prosaically, then cursed herself as she found she was hanging on to the phone in a white-knuckled clench until well after the dial tone was ringing in her ear.

"Idiot!" she muttered as she threw the phone back down on the hook. "What do you think you're doing, Ellen Bowman!"

She kept on muttering vile imprecations upon herself as she finished her cleaning, but nothing could still the nervous, burgeoning excitement she felt at the thought of seeing Ross again. "Fool!" rang through the house more than once, and the dust flew as she threw herself into her cleaning with a vengeance, her habitual remedy for dispelling disturbing thoughts.

But, surprisingly, on the day of the picnic, the closer she got to Ross's ranch, the calmer she grew. She loved the drive through the rolling Flint Hills, which were just turning themselves into paeans to spring, and she felt a sense of release as the lovely scents and warm breeze caressed her hair and skin as she drove along with her window down.

Rosie and Jake had offered her a ride, and Ellen still wasn't prepared to be honest with herself about why she had turned them down. The excuse she had used—that of wanting to start later than they did because she had some things to attend to—should have screamed its dishonesty at her with a clarion call, but she blithely ignored it and promptly invented something to make it true.

She felt better than she had for ages as she turned off on the two-lane country road leading to Ross's ranch, and she accepted the feeling without delving too deeply into why it should be so. And when she pulled up behind Jake and Rosie's van and climbed out of her Corvette, her smile would have lit up a dark cave had she been in one rather than standing outside a lovely, natural stone ranch house in the midst of a glorious Kansas countryside.

It grew even brighter as she saw Ross striding toward her in tight, faded bluejeans, cowboy boots, a worn leather belt, and a light blue, long-sleeve shirt that matched his eyes. He had rolled up the sleeves of the shirt and the sun glinted off the golden hairs on his strong, tanned, muscled arms and off the shock of thick blond hair she wanted to run her fingers through at that very moment. His mustache was the same, his eyes were the same, and she promptly, in one blinding instant, fell head over heels in love with him!

Though slightly stunned by the knowledge that flooded through her in a tide of mingled joy and alarm, Ellen nevertheless managed to greet him with a semblance of sanity. "Hi, Ross. Come to see if I've brought my ticket to the picnic?" she asked on a gurgling chuckle that echoed the light shining from her clear, and, right now, almost green eyes.

"The price has gone up," he drawled as he came to a stop in front of her and eyed her up and down with a male appreciation that brought a pink flush of pleasure to her cheeks. She was dressed simply in a short-sleeve white blouse and jeans and cowboy boots with her long, thick hair in two slender braids meeting at the back of her head, but Ross's gaze made her feel as though she were standing before him in the sheerest of negligees and she felt a weakening beginning in her knees and a heat start up in the region of her pelvis that threatened to make her throw herself into his arms.

"That's not fair," she said with pouting gravity. "I think that comes under false advertising."

"Why?" he said in a lazy, amused, intimate drawl. "You've got the coin to pay it with you."

"What is the price then?" she asked dubiously.

"This . . ." he said in a teasing whisper as he took her shoulders into his warm hands and pulled her slightly toward him while he lowered his lips to her mouth.

Ellen's face had gone pale, and her eyes were drugged with wanting by the time he raised his head, and he viewed both with masculine satisfaction before he released her. "It's still there, isn't it?" he murmured in a low tone of pleasure, his eyes daring her to deny it.

"I'm afraid so," she replied on an aching sigh of resignation as she gazed back at him almost reproachfully.

"Good," he murmured in a teasing, satisfied tone. "I've doubted my sanity more than once in the past few months."

And on that enigmatic note he passed her to go to the car and get the box of food she had brought with her, then gestured with his head for her to accompany him as he started back to the house.

"Is everyone else here?" she asked, straining for casualness.

"Yep, can't you hear them?" he chuckled, referring to some high-pitched squeals from Bill and Marie's toddlers coming from the house.

A soft smile crossed Ellen's mouth as she listened. She adored children, and she was looking forward to their presence at this day's entertainment. "Did Peg and Randy bring the baby?" she asked happily, her earlier discomfort draining away in anticipation of a day spent outdoors in a glorious setting with people she cared about . . . particularly one of them.

"Ummm-hmmm," he answered almost absently, though he shot her a look from under his brows that would have puzzled her had she seen it. But she was too busy looking around her to notice. "Can you get the door?" he asked when they got to the house.

"Sure," she answered cheerfully, and a moment later was engulfed by the rest of the party, Jake rushing forward to retrieve her box of food from Ross's grip. Ross released it with a grunt of laughter at Jake's greed. "What do you say we get started, everybody?" he asked the others. "We're all here now."

To Ellen's delight, Ross had provided horses for those who wanted to ride to the river, and a jeep to transport the food and the ones who didn't. She elected to ride, as did Ross, and she filled her eyes with the sight of him as he controlled his beautiful roan gelding with the ease and strength of a born rider.

The setting for the picnic was delightful. Ross had had an area of prairie grass mowed to provide a smooth surface near some trees and within sight of the clear, slow-moving river rippling over its stony bed. Bill and Marie's

67

children ran shrieking over the grass as though their souls had been set free in this open setting, and Ellen felt like doing the same.

Everyone was in an easy mood, each responding to the natural atmosphere around them in a positive way, and while the women laid out the food, the men walked down to the river to talk lazily of crops and cattle and business and politics. They came eagerly back when the women called to tell them the meal was ready, and everyone settled down around the checked tablecloth to eat fried chicken, baked beans, potato salad, and cole slaw, all making pigs of themselves until it was agreed the dessert would have to wait awhile.

Peg's baby was a little fretful, as he was cutting a new tooth, and when Ellen caught sight of her friend's rather harried face, she moved to take the child from her and started strolling down to the river, humming and gently jiggling his small form with tender sympathy. She settled down beneath a tree with her back leaning against the bole and proceeded to devote her whole attention to bettering the poor little mite's mood.

She was astonished, then seized with helpless giggles when the baby, apparently deciding he needed more substantial comfort, began to nuzzle at her breast imperiously, his small hands scrabbling at the impediment of her shirt in frustration. He was beginning to whimper when a shadow loomed over them and Ellen raised her face, convulsed with laughter to see Ross staring down at her and the baby with an enigmatic expression that reduced her laughter to a smile.

"I take it Peg breastfeeds him," he commented in a dry, amused tone as he squatted down and placed a caressing hand on the baby's back.

"Yes," Ellen gurgled, then yelped as the baby's small, sharp nails scraped the sensitive skin between her breasts.

Ross grinned, but the grin slowly faded away to be replaced with an almost sober contemplation as he watched the baby continue to scrabble at Ellen's breast. "The little son of a gun is determined, isn't he?" he said with soft musing, his eyes turning a darker blue as a swipe of the child's fist pushed the white material back from Ellen's breast, exposing part of its rounded fullness. "I can't say as I blame him," he said even more softly, his gaze lifting to Ellen's, its heat causing her to catch her breath.

"I—I guess I'd better give him back to his mother," Ellen faltered, her heart rate increasing in direct proportion to Ross's probing, intense gaze. "He's . . . he's hungry," she offered tentatively.

"He's not the only one," Ross murmured seductively, his mouth quirking with sardonic humor that was not quite amused beneath his mustache. Ellen watched the movement with fascination, her mind sheering off into an insane contemplation of what it would be like to have that mouth and that mustache at her breast. Their lovemaking on the ski trip had been so intense and so precipitate, she had not had that pleasure, and she wanted it now with an aching need that shone clearly from her eyes as she sat there completely caught up in Ross's spell.

Someone called to them then, breaking the magic of the moment, and Ellen sat up in preparation to get up and return the baby to his mother. But as her gaze dropped from Ross's, it fell upon his lower body, and she gave an involuntary gasp as she saw that he was every bit as aroused as he had been that day months ago when he had taken her with such gut-wrenching passion.

"Yes." He nodded his head as he saw where her eyes were focussed. "You still have the same effect on me." He rose to his feet in one fluid, powerful motion, pausing slightly as her eyes followed him, allowing her to see what so fascinated her with a natural lack of embarrassment that made it easier for her to accept her own need to look at him. Then he turned away slightly, his back to the others still at the picnic lunch.

"You go on," he drawled with soft amusement. "I think I'd better take a short walk until I can present myself to the others without embarrassing the hell out of them."

Ellen shut her eyes for a moment as he started off ambling down toward the riverbank, shaken by his effect on her, though she reminded herself she should have expected it, especially since she had just accepted that she was in love with him. Then she got to her feet and hugged the baby to her a moment for comfort as she gazed after Ross with sad longing in her eyes.

You fool, she muttered to herself achingly. *There are men all over the country to fall in love with. So why did you have to pick one who's not the slightest bit interested in anything but a hot, flaming affair that would tear you to pieces within a month!*

With a shake of her head in despair at her own idiocy, Ellen made her way back to the others and handed over the starving baby to his mother, who chuckled when Ellen told her how she knew he was hungry. "You little squirt!" she scolded her son in a mock stern voice. "Don't you have any loyalty to your own mother?" Whereupon the men in the company laughed and leered at Ellen suggestively, Jake remarking that the boy showed a great deal of sense, variety being the spice of life and all. Which earned him a scorching look from his wife and groans from Ellen and Peg.

The rest of the day passed pleasantly enough for Ellen, but she found her eyes resting on Ross far too often for comfort, and as they gathered up the remains of the picnic and started back, she could only hope no one else, most particularly Ross, had noticed her preoccupation with

70

him. She was feeling desolate at the thought of climbing back into her car and returning to her now lonely-seeming house, when he caught up with her just as she was riding into the corral where they would dismount the horses.

"Stay over for a few minutes, will you?" he asked casually, in a low, soft voice no one else could hear. "I want to talk to you."

Her heart giving a little burst of excitement and relief that she could be with him for just a little longer, Ellen nodded, and he pulled away from her. Half an hour later, the two of them stood in the front yard waving after Jake and Rosie, who were the last to depart, and Ellen was trying not to think about the delighted, mischievous interest Rosie had shown when she realized Ellen wasn't leaving yet.

Ellen leaned back against the split-rail fence as the van disappeared down the road, her eyes squinting against a glorious sunset that colored wisps of clouds a fiery crimson. Her attention was diverted sharply, however, when Ross came to stand in front of her, placing his hands on the fence on either side of her and effectively hemming her in, though he made no move to touch other than with his eyes.

"I hear you've been dating," he started off, his voice seemingly calm, but with a little thread of danger beneath it that had Ellen blinking up at him in confusion.

"Yes," she admitted with a noncommittal shrug.

He seemed to be waiting for her to say something else, and when she didn't, his jaw tightened almost imperceptibly, though his voice was still calm, as he said, "Well?"

Ellen stared at him, wondering what he wanted. "Well, what?" she asked a little helplessly.

"Are you *enjoying* the single life?" he said, his voice turning just the slightest bit grim.

Ellen shrugged, wondering how honest she should be,

then deciding it made little difference how honest she was. "No, not really," she said in a small voice.

"Why not?" he persisted, and Ellen shifted restlessly where she stood, wondering at the reason for this inquisition.

"I . . . haven't met anyone I want to go to bed with, and that seems to be all they *do* want," she said with a trace of exasperation. Then, her own jaw firming, she lifted her chin and looked him directly in the eye. "How about you, Ross? How's your love life?" she asked, a tinge sarcastically.

"If you're asking me if I've had sex lately, the answer is yes," he said with a calm that made her tense with jealousy. "Once or twice, after a night of the damned dreams I seem to have become stuck with since I gave a certain woman a massage that turned out to be a lot more than either of us had bargained for. I've had to obtain some kind of relief or go stark, raving mad," he informed her, still in that same calm, soft voice that seemed so incongruous when he was telling her she had haunted his dreams for the past few months. "And you're a little liar," he finished with an unamused quirk of his mouth under the mustache.

"Wh—what?" Ellen asked, trying to assimilate what he'd said and taken completely by surprise by his ending statement.

"You have met one person you want to go to bed with, haven't you, Ellen?" he asked meaningfully, and when she dropped her eyes and tried to look away from him, he raised a hand to cup her chin and turn her back to him. "I'd be willing to bet your own dreams haven't been exactly peaceful in the last few months either, have they, Ellen?"

The sexy, husky timbre of his voice chased chills down her spine, and the answering desire that shot through her veins was communicated clearly to him by the frantic pulse in her throat, the slow cloud of passion that began to veil her eyes, and the way her mouth parted slightly to let her tongue slip out and wet her lips.

"Ellen . . ." he murmured warningly, his eyes watching the movement of her tongue as though hypnotized. "Don't provoke me like that unless you're ready to take the consequences." And when she gazed up at him helplessly, he gave a little groan and dipped his head to take over the task of moistening her mouth himself, and Ellen knew it was already too late to stop herself from provoking him into giving her exactly what she wanted.

She let her mouth play with his, enjoying to the full each tender taste, each mobile movement of his mouth against hers, and she felt unbearably disappointed when, although his breath was coming raspingly through his lips, he drew back slightly to look into her eyes.

"I haven't changed my mind about marriage yet, Ellen," he whispered softly to her. "But I want you very, very badly tonight. And you want me. Will you stay with me this once? Let me make love to you for a whole night, so that I don't have to wake up in the middle of a dream and reach for you and find again that you're not there?"

His words melted her heart and her answering, "Yes, Ross, I'll stay with you tonight," was delivered in a tender, crooning song of love that had him gathering her up into his arms before the last word had left her lips.

"God, I've missed you!" he said in a rasping tone under his breath as he kissed her again while he walked to the door of his house and carried her through it. "I don't know what I'd have done if you'd said no."

She didn't tell him that it would have been impossible for her to say no to him on this first day she had discovered her love for him. She only whispered back that she had missed him, too, then drowned in his kiss as he carried her

73

through the house to his bedroom, where he set her gently on her feet beside his bed.

His hands were on the buttons of her shirt when she asked him hesitantly, in a low voice, "Can we . . . go slower this time, Ross? I want . . . I need . . ." She didn't know how to tell him what was in her heart, but he seemed to understand, and his voice was gentle when he answered.

"I don't know about the first time, honey. Once I have my hands on you after all this time, I can't be responsible for what will happen. But the next time . . . and the next . . . I promise you we'll go as slow as you want. I want it too. You wouldn't believe what I've been doing to you almost every night for months now. It's about time I got a chance to put some of it into practice."

Her smile was tremulous as he divested her of her last article of clothing, then lifted her hands to his, inviting her to do the same for him, while he took inventory with his eyes and his hands, making love to her with both until she was all thumbs and he had to help her finish undressing him. And once they were on the bed together, Ross did try to take it slow, as she had asked him to, but it was Ellen who couldn't rein in the bursting, surging need his merest touch provoked, and it was she who forced him to abandon the slow, sensual seduction he was engaged in and replace it with an urgent, spiraling passion that brought them both to an explosive culmination that left them gasping for breath, their muscles trembling with reaction to their lovemaking, their skins slick with the perspiration of love.

Shamed by her riotous greed, Ellen started to mumble an apology, and Ross's exultant chuckle absolved her of blame. "Do you think I'm disappointed?" he asked with indulgent incredulity. "Don't you think I needed that as much as you did? I wouldn't have lasted much longer in any case," he added, his smile tender as he gathered her into his arms. "I was doing my best, but if you hadn't broken the traces, I would have."

She smiled, comforted by his reassurance, pleased by his admission that she excited him as much as he did her. It provoked her into an admission of her own. "It *was* nice to have the reality instead of the dream, wasn't it?" she murmured half-teasingly, half-seriously.

"Ah, so you have been having an active night life, after all?" he teased her back, his hand cupping her breast possessively. "Am I the only man in your dreams, sweetheart?"

She nodded against his shoulder. "The only one," she admitted, husky sleepiness mumbling her voice.

"Are you going to sleep on me?" he asked gently.

"Not if you don't want me to," she said in the middle of a yawn.

He gave a soft laugh and cuddled her against him. "Make it a short nap, then, honey," he whispered in a growl. "I can't spare you for very long." And as she dropped off, it was with a smile, one that Ross traced with a gentle finger as he closed his own eyes to savor the feel of her lying in his arms at last, after too many long nights without her.

It did turn out to be a short nap, because Ross wouldn't leave her alone. He kept touching her, stroking her, and kissing her until Ellen swam up out of her doze and began to reciprocate, each of them exploring with an unselfconscious delight in getting to know each other's bodies and in learning the particular pleasures of the other that made the night a magic segment out of time.

"I never would have believed a mustache could be so versatile," Ellen murmured with warm teasing when at last they had succeeded in pushing their mutual exploration past the point of aroused appreciation and into the realm of single-minded desperation and were now once again free to communicate with normal, though weary, coherence.

Ross stroked his mustache with a languid finger and gazed down at her with mischief in his eyes. "You ain't seen nothin' yet," he promised with a leering waggle of his eyebrows.

"Ohhh . . ." Ellen managed a despairing look and exaggerated weariness in her tone. "You've got to be kidding! I'm only a poor little female, Ross, remember that. We're the weaker sex, you know?"

The solemn gravity in her tone brought a sceptical look to Ross's face. "That was weak?" he said dubiously, then shook his head in disagreement. "Sorry, but it didn't seem like it to me."

Ellen batted her eyes up at him with exaggerated feminine flirtatiousness. "You inspired me to exert myself past my normal limits," she said demurely. "You're such a strong, manly, handsome, clever . . ."

He cut off her syrupy venture into the realm of female flattery with a hard look, and then a hard kiss with Ellen dissolving into giggles under his mouth. "What's the matter?" she asked innocently when at last he raised his head. "Don't you like a little sincere praise from a woman who's swooning beneath the devastation of your charm?"

"*Sincere* is the operative word," he responded wryly. "I like the way your body says it better." And then he gathered her up into his arms for a gentle, warming cuddle that filled a need in Ellen every bit as compelling as his demands had inspired earlier, and as she responded in a way that showed her pleasure, a smile lifted Ross's mouth into a contented curve.

"See what I mean?" he murmured with deep satisfaction. "Your body never lies. Sometimes I think this is the best part of loving, though Tina never . . ."

He broke off what he had been about to say, and Ellen,

feeling a chill at his introducing his ex-wife's name into their intimacy, glanced up to see a frown creasing his forehead, replacing his former smile. For a moment she debated remaining silent, but found the words leaving her lips before she knew they were coming.

"Tina wasn't . . . ah . . . affectionate?" she asked hesitantly, her voice revealing a quiet distress.

After a pause, Ross answered, his voice dry. "No. Tina wasn't affectionate. Tina wasn't a lot of things, as a matter of fact." Then he arched a glance down at her, his tone thoughtful as he asked, "But I imagine John was, wasn't he?"

Feeling more disturbed by the moment, Ellen nodded her head. "Very," she said softly, and then, without meaning to, started to withdraw her body from his.

"Don't . . ." he said, sounding regretful that he had introduced something between them that was destroying their closeness. "I'm sorry that slipped out. Come back, Ellen," he whispered, exerting his strength to draw her back to him again. "Let's not let the past ruin tonight. It's been too long coming and it was much too perfect before I . . ." He stopped speaking and let his mouth tell her more effectively than words could what he meant.

CHAPTER SEVEN

Ellen sat across from Ross at the breakfast table watching him devour a huge meal while she sipped a cup of coffee and prepared herself to leave his house and his life for good. She had been surprised and pleased when he had wakened her with a kiss that morning and informed her he had breakfast ready, which meant that he wasn't quite the male chauvinist she had judged him to be. But learning new things to love about him only increased her distress at having been so foolish as to fall in love with him when she had known he wasn't willing to become involved with her except on a physical basis. And while she didn't, couldn't, regret giving in to their mutual desire the preceding night, it only added to the difficulties of today.

"You're looking sad, Ellen," Ross addressed her with warm concern. "Are you having regrets about last night?"

Dismayed that she had let him see, however inadvertently, some of the turmoil going on inside her, Ellen attempted a bright smile. "No, of course not, Ross. It was lovely." But while the warmth in her eyes and tone conveyed the sincerity of her words, there was still a sadness there as well that Ross picked up on. He leaned back in his chair and studied her, his expression showing that he was not immune to some of the torment that afflicted her.

"Then why do I have the feeling you don't intend to repeat last night?" he asked softly. "At least not without the prospect of a proposal of marriage as the price I'd have to pay to get you here again?"

Suffused with anger and hurt at Ross's blunt insensitivity, Ellen slammed her coffee cup down on the table. "I've never asked you for anything, Ross Sayer!" she blurted out impetuously. "And I have no intention of doing so. I didn't even ask to become involved with you at all, if you remember, and you've known from the start I didn't want an affair with you or anyone else!" Angry tears glistened in her hazel eyes, and she raised an impatient hand to brush them away, words still sputtering on her lips. "You needn't imply I'm playing some underhanded female game with you to get you to make a commitment you don't want! I'm not Tina!"

The last statement was filled with the scathing contempt Ellen felt for Ross's ex-wife and, after making it, though she was a little appalled at her own bluntness, she felt disinclined to back down from what was, after all, an honest opinion. Therefore, she folded her arms across her chest and settled back to glare at Ross with indignant challenge in every line of her slender body.

His rather disconcerting reaction was to breathe a silent curse as he ran an impatient hand through his thick hair, and then to apologize, something Ellen certainly hadn't expected, if she'd known what to expect at all!

"Sorry, honey," he said as he gave a wry grimace of self-denunciation. "I know you've been up front with me, and I appreciate it. It's a welcome change from—" He broke off what he'd been about to say, but Ellen was certain he had been about to admit that Tina *had* played just the sort of games Ellen had mentioned. "It's just that I'm feeling frustrated because I can't have what I want on my terms," he admitted with dry honesty. "And I do want you, Ellen . . . more than ever now," he finished softly.

Mollified by Ross's apology and by his admission of

how attracted he was to her, Ellen let her anger slide away to be replaced by a sad frustration of her own. "I know, Ross," she echoed his soft tone. "I want you too." She hesitated a moment, forming words in her mind to try to explain her position without giving away her newly discovered love for him. She needed the protection of keeping her innermost feelings to herself, and, besides, she wasn't sure whether such an admission would lead Ross to use it to further his own ends, in a very human manner, or whether it would lead him to feel guilty at having elicited such an emotion from her.

"I want to get married again, Ross," she temporized, not telling him that it was he she wanted to marry. "I miss the warmth, the closeness, the commitment . . . and, yes," she admitted further, dropping her eyes to contemplate her hands, "I miss making love." She didn't say that that was what she had done the night before, knowing as she did that Ross had only been having sex. "An affair with you is tempting, but . . ." She fell silent, unable to find the words to conceal the truth, that an affair with him would be an emotional disaster as far as she was concerned. She knew she would inevitably fall more and more in love with him and yet ultimately be faced with the same dilemma she had to deal with now, the necessity of putting her feelings for him behind her and continuing her search for someone who was prepared to offer her more than a warm, tempting body in her bed.

"But . . ." he echoed on a sigh of resignation, his expression grimly frustrated. "That's a big word, and one that applies to me too. If I hadn't had such a bad experience with Tina, or if you weren't the sort of woman you are and John's widow to boot . . ." He gave a grunt and scraped his chair back to stand up. "But I did and you are, so . . ."

Ellen nodded, keeping her eyes down so that he

wouldn't see how utterly depressed she was feeling. He came around the table toward her, and she made a supreme effort to clear her thoughts and feelings from her face to look at him calmly. "So it's best if we say good-bye now, Ross, don't you agree?" she asked levelly.

"I don't know about it being best, but it seems to be the only choice open at the moment," he responded dryly as he reached down to grasp her shoulders and draw her to her feet. He wrapped his arms around her, and his eyes memorized her as he gazed down at her upturned face. "It isn't going to be easy," he murmured quietly. "I don't want to think of you being with another man. I don't want to go through more nights of having you in my dreams but not in my arms. I want you with me, Ellen."

Though her expression remained impassive, Ellen was screaming at him inwardly, asking him *why* then he couldn't at least make the attempt to get over the legacy of hurt and suspicion Tina had left behind her. But an instant later she realized it was better this way. Suppose he did make the attempt and didn't succeed? In that case, she would be right back where she was now, only more embroiled than ever in loving him to no purpose.

He rested his forehead against hers, holding her quietly for a few moments before he lifted his head again. "Kiss me good-bye then, Ellen," he whispered roughly. "And then get out of here before I promise you anything to keep you from going!"

Without waiting for her to do as he instructed, his mouth seized hers in an almost brutal kiss, containing his frustration, his desire for her, and his self-directed anger, and then, much too soón, he was thrusting her away from him and turning on his heel to leave the room and the house to go about his work.

Ellen watched him go, one hand raised to her mouth as though to protect the last kiss she would receive from him, her eyes huge and filling with the tears she had suppressed so long. Then, she, too, turned abruptly to collect her things before she dashed out to her car, started the motor, and kicked up dust from the wheels as she drove furiously away from what threatened to pull her back against all reason.

As the miles sped by and she managed to choke down her regret and her tears, she gave a faint smile of sad resignation. "Well, you'd be proud of me, John," she whispered to the empty interior of the car. "You always said I had more than my share of will power, and if this doesn't prove it, I don't know what will."

But she knew there would be months of having to exert that will power before she was safely over the dangerous pull Ross Sayer exerted so strongly, if she would ever be safe from his brand of attraction again.

CHAPTER EIGHT

The next few weeks proved to be as bad as Ellen had anticipated, her days tinged with loneliness no matter how busy she kept herself, and her nights almost literally unbearable. At first, she dated with concentrated singleness of mind, hoping against hope there would be one man somewhere who could erase Ross from her heart sufficiently to grant her peace from her incessant thoughts of him. When that didn't happen, she dropped the tactic, preferring her own company or that of her friends to spending her evenings with one after another man who merely left her impatient and frustrated.

Fortunately, as the campaign for her gubernatorial candidate heated up, she found herself more and more involved in volunteer work for him, and it was in that connection that she finally saw Ross once again. She was sponsoring a fund-raising dinner for the candidate, and since it was her job to dragoon as many people as possible into attending the dinner, it seemed quite natural, considering Ross's professed preference for her candidate, to invite him as well. At least that was what she told herself as she nervously dialed his number and swallowed down the knot of fear in her throat.

She closed her eyes against a wave of longing when she heard his deep voice answering the call, and it was a moment before she could make herself speak. "Hello?" he said again, his tones indicating a growing impatience, and Ellen cleared her throat to answer him.

"Ross?" she asked unnecessarily. "It's Ellen."

It was his turn to remain silent for a long moment then, and Ellen's to ask, hesitantly, "Ross?"

"I'm here," he answered, his tone conveying absolutely nothing other than exactly what he'd said.

"I . . . ah . . . how are you?" Ellen faltered, beginning to feel rather desperate at the lack of expression he was displaying and beginning to wish also that she had never given in to the insane idea that she could handle speaking to him again.

"Fine." His clipped reply sparked the start of a growing anger inside Ellen that he could be so unforthcoming after the intimacy they'd shared. That anger gave her the courage to get to the point of her call and get off the line, once and for all!

"Good," she replied, her tone as clipped as his now. "Are you still in Joel Blake's camp as a political candidate, Ross?"

She was sulkily gratified to hear the puzzlement in Ross's tone when he replied. "Joel Blake? Why, yes, I intend to vote for him anyway. Why do you—"

She cut him off, all brisk and businesslike now. "Good! Are you willing to put your pocketbook where your convictions are?" she asked breezily.

"Within reason," came his dry reply. "Why do you ask?"

"I'm working for his campaign," Ellen explained matter-of-factly, "and I'm sponsoring a fund-raising dinner for him on the twenty-fifth. Are you willing to come? I warn you, the tickets aren't cheap," she added with a martyred sense of fairness.

It had never occurred to her that Ross would take her well-meaning warning as a slam against him personally, but it was clear he had done so from the tone of his reply. "Gee, I don't know," he said with dry, nasty sarcasm. "Maybe if I sold off a few cattle and an acre or so of pasture, I just might be able to swing it, but you'll have to tell me how much first, so I'll know whether I can afford to join such an illustrious company as yourself and our esteemed candidate."

Stricken by her own tactlessness, Ellen started to say, "Ross, I didn't mean—" but he cut her off in mid-sentence.

"The hell you didn't! How much are the damned tickets, Ellen?"

The rasping harshness in his tone quelled her desire to apologize and Ellen named the sum in a small, stiff voice.

"Fine," he said cuttingly. "I'll have a check in the mail to you tomorrow. Is that all, ma'am?"

Stung by that last little touch of sarcasm, Ellen answered with deadly sweetness. "Why, no, Mr. Sayer, it isn't. Do you think you can *afford* to bring a date as well? You can consider it your patriotic duty if the burden seems too heavy!"

Her display of temper backfired badly, however, when, after a moment of dead silence, Ross came back at her with a nasty chuckle. "I'd be delighted to do my duty, ma'am," he drawled. "I have just the person in mind, and I expect I'll be well repaid for treating her to a dinner with the elite."

"Lovely," Ellen grated out, barely able to restrain her urge to treat him to a display of bad language that might make even *his* ears turn a little red. "Just double the amount I told you and put the check in the mail. Mr. Blake and I will be delighted to accept your support!"

"*He* might be," Ross admitted sardonically, "but you don't need it, Miss Moneybags. See you in two weeks." Whereupon he promptly hung up in her ear, leaving Ellen to glare down at the receiver with all the venom of a poisonous snake.

Her anger evaporated rapidly, however, as she contemplated the thought of seeing Ross with another woman, and all because she hadn't been able to control her own stupid tongue.

"Twit!" she castigated herself grimly as she paced back and forth, back and forth over the living room carpet. "Idiot!" she castigated Ross an instant later as she felt a frustrated sense of injustice over his sensitivity where her financial resources were concerned. She had no idea how much he himself was worth, but she knew ranchers were often at the mercy of the prevailing market price for beef, flush one year perhaps and on the verge of bankruptcy the next.

She seated herself on the sofa and gazed forlornly at the empty fireplace, wondering why men like Ross had to equate their manliness with their wallets. Didn't he realize he would stand head and shoulders over most men whether he had a penny to his name? She switched her gaze to John and smiled at his portrait wanly, blessing his memory with gratitude that he hadn't been so inclined. Their joint philosophy had been that whatever resources came to one of them belonged to both to be shared equally.

Well, she thought to herself now, gloomily resigned, Ross's chauvinism regarding money was just one more indication that they weren't destined to share their lives. She should be grateful at receiving that indication and use it to stiffen her flagging backbone. She straightened unconsciously in reaction to her thoughts and scowled at an inoffensive fig tree in front of the window. And if Ross Sayer thought he was going to cause her any undue distress by escorting another woman to the dinner, he had another think coming. She had a defense or two of her own to put into practice!

So deciding, she braced herself to go to the telephone and dial the number of one of the most handsome, most urbane and charming, and most dedicatedly mercenary of the men she had dated during the past few months. He might be a hell of a lot more interested in her bank balance than in any of her more sterling qualities, but Ross Sayer wouldn't know that! All he would know was that she was being escorted by a stunningly impressive man who would make Ross's date fade into insignificance, she hoped.

When the night of the dinner arrived, Ellen went all out on her own appearance, paying a visit to the hairdresser, decking herself out in new, expensive clothing, and paying particular attention to her makeup. When at last she stood back from the mirror to view herself with anxious expectation that she would fall short of what she wished for, just as she always had, she instead found herself blinking in pleased smugness at the effect she had managed to create.

Her mass of hair was gathered at the back of her head in a charmingly sophisticated loose bun with tendrils gently caressing the nape of her neck and her well-formed ears, each of which sported a sparkling diamond earring which, though they had cost her a bundle, she now considered worth every penny. Her eyes, shaded with green shadow, looked mysteriously sparkling behind the fringe of long, darkened lashes she now batted flirtatiously with mischievous glee, while her moist, pink mouth curved seductively into a smile she was willing to bet even her soon-to-arrive escort would view with as least as much interest as he did her purse.

The dress, a slender, figure-hugging masterpiece of style, glimmered its metallic invitation at her every movement, the swirling strips of green interspersed with silver enhancing the color of her eyes until the brown in them was almost totally eclipsed by a fascinating emerald shade. And last, but not least, her slender, delicate feet were encased in high-heeled silver sandals that brought her height up to at least six feet, which made her doubly grateful her escort's attractiveness included the distinction of being at least six two.

Nodding her head with satisfaction, Ellen reflected that she and Marcus Fielding should turn a few heads tonight through that fact alone, though she didn't care a fig about anyone's attention other than Ross Sayer's. But where he was concerned, she wanted not only to turn his head in her direction, but his whole magnificent body as well, and since she couldn't recall one occasion in their past where he had seen her looking even remotely as stunning as she did tonight, she hoped that wouldn't prove too difficult.

The doorbell interrupted her self-absorbed thoughts, and she caught up a silver stole to match her dress and hurried to the door to admit the man for whom tonight might be the first occasion in his life where *he* was being used rather than being the user. Ellen felt no qualms about making such use of him, since she had taken his measure on their very first, and only, preceding date, and had dismissed him with offhanded impatience as the most egotistical, asinine, mercenary man she had ever had the mispleasure of meeting in her entire life!

"Marcus!" she greeted him with a beaming smile of pleasure as she ran her eyes over his tuxedoed figure approvingly.

"Ellen, my dear." Marcus greeted her with a charmingly calculated smile that he meant to devastate her in her tracks. Though he thought he had succeeded when her smile grew more welcoming by the moment, he had no way of knowing the smile was simply a result of her satisfaction at seeing he was just as outwardly attractive as she remembered.

He bent to kiss her and Ellen managed to deflect the kiss so that it fell on her cheek instead of her mouth. He laughed a small, self-confident laugh and gazed down at her complacently. "Still as shy as ever, I see," he said indulgently.

Still as conceited as a fatbreasted peacock, I see, Ellen answered him in her thoughts while she managed a shy smile. "I think we're on the verge of being late, Marcus," she said instead. "Do you mind very much if I don't invite you in for a drink?"

That Marcus was not pleased at being subverted in the campaign to win her over was apparent in the slight scowl that flickered over his handsome face. "Late?" he asked distastefully. "I'm sure we're not, Ellen. Why it's only . . ."

"Yes, but I have to be there early to make sure all the arrangements have been made correctly," Ellen said with a sweet smile. "I'm one of the hostesses, you know."

Confronted with that, Marcus could hardly object, though his compliance seemed to be rather grudging. Ellen hid a smile as she realized he had probably planned on using the few moments they would have had in her living room to make a stab at overcoming her "shyness." She was more than happy to deny him the opportunity and was already planning a timely headache to thwart the similar attempt she knew would be forthcoming at the end of the evening.

By the time Ross and his date arrived at the dinner, Ellen was feeling her oats to an unconscionable degree. Having been the recipient of so many sincere compliments on her appearance, she was in danger of having her head turned by them. The woman clinging proprietarily to Ross's arm brought Ellen up short, however, and within seconds Ellen was having to strain to maintain her smile and her aura of sophisticated glamor as well.

For one thing, Ross's date was petite. Her gleaming dark curls came just to his bicep, and she looked so devastatingly feminine when she gazed up at Ross adoringly, Ellen suddenly felt like the Jolly Green Giant. In addition, the woman's resemblance to Tina was so marked, Ellen had the despairing sense that no other sort of woman would ever attract Ross to any great and lasting degree. Too, there was a sly-cat complacency about the woman and an intimacy in the looks she gave Ross that spelled out little short of screaming that that intimacy hadn't been confined to just looking!

The last straw was that Ross himself, clad in a form-hugging tuxedo that made him look like a male model in a glossy magazine ad, was so much more devastatingly appealing than she had believed he could be, Ellen was thrown into such a fit of the glooms that the slow, below-the-breath expletive she exhaled implied that the world was coming to an end.

"What's the matter with you all of a sudden?" Rosie said into her ear, having come up beside her while Ellen was involved in her contemplation of Ross and his date. "A minute ago you sparkled like a Fourth of July candle. Now you look like you've just lost your best friend."

Rosie's observation alerted Ellen that she had better act her heart out if she wanted to maintain the image of glamorous, lighthearted contentment she had meant to portray for Ross's benefit. She turned a bright smile on Rosie and said with casual affection, "You're my best friend, Rosie. I haven't lost you, have I?"

Rosie looked down at herself comically and quipped, "Not that I'd noticed. In fact, I seem to be growing if anything." Then she shrugged and smiled slyly. "They say that's what happens to prospective mothers though, so I guess I should have expected it."

Ellen blinked at her friend in astonishment, then grinned in unmitigated joy at her news. Rosie and Jake had been trying to have a child for years, and the knowledge that they were finally going to succeed was a delight to Ellen. "Rosie, how wonderful!" she gasped with spontaneous joy. "How long have you known?" She was hugging Rosie uninhibitedly as she said this when over her shoulder she saw Ross looking in her direction. She scowled momentarily, then wiped her expression away, determined that the man wasn't going to spoil the good feelings she was having for the first time since he had entered the room.

"I just found out today," Rosie crowed her satisfaction. "And if you think you're happy, take a look at Jake!"

Whereupon Ellen sought out her portly friend with her eyes to see him positively glowing with happiness, his broad face split in a wall-to-wall grin that threatened to split the seams. "Bless him!" Ellen chortled. "He really doesn't have a poker face, does he?"

"You can say that again." Rosie beamed her husband a look of love. "But I wouldn't change a thing about him . . . except maybe his waistline," she added with a wifely frown.

Ellen laughed and hugged Rosie again. "No, you wouldn't," she teased her friend gaily. "Jake wouldn't be Jake without that roll around his stomach, and you know it."

Rosie opened her mouth to protest such a declaration, but at that moment Ross came up behind her and put a friendly arm around her shoulders. "What's going on here?" he drawled in a teasing vein. "Have you two been into the liquor or are you just in a good mood?"

Ellen kept her smile friendly and bland though her muscles ached with the effort when she saw Ross gaze at her without a flicker of more than token greeting. Fortunately, Rosie was full of her own news and monopolized the conversation so that Ellen didn't have to speak.

"I'm finally going to have a baby, Ross," she chirped,

giving him a hug to express her exuberance. "And Jake's going to be a proud papa at last."

Ellen fell in love with Ross all over again when she saw his reaction to the news. Wrapping his arms around the ecstatic Rosie, he gave her a whopping squeeze and a heartfelt, "Good for you, Rosie! Now *I'll* finally get to be a godfather!"

An instant later, Ellen's bemused smile as she watched Ross hug Rosie faded as Rosie replied, her eyes slyly mischievous, "Yes, and Ellen will be the godmother. Maybe that shared responsibility will finally bring the two of you closer."

Ellen shot Rosie a suspicious look, but though she suspected her exuberant friend of knowing more of what had gone on between herself and Ross than had ever been discussed, there was nothing she could say. At any rate, Marcus returned at that moment from fetching her a drink, and she turned to him with a melting look of gratitude for the rescue from this awkward situation. She took her drink, tucked her hand under his arm, and turned back to Rosie, Ross, and Ross's date, graciously performing introductions.

"Rosie . . . Ross . . . I'd like you to meet Marcus Fielding." And after that introduction had been made, Ellen turned her gaze in the direction of Ross's date, her look inquiring.

"This is Freda Sterling." Ross performed his own introductions smoothly, giving the tiny woman by his side an indulgent look while he covered the hand she had on his arm with one of his own.

Ellen's sense of hope, which had been engendered by the distinctly cool, challenging look Ross had given Marcus, died a gloomy death. *Damn him!* she thought all the while she was smiling blandly at his date. *It would serve him right if he fell for this disgusting reincarnation of Tina!*

92

She was saved from any further close contact with Ross and the woman Ellen had immediately detested when the candidate himself finally arrived, and she and Marcus moved to greet him. From then on the evening was a whirling blur. She and Marcus were seated at the head table with Joel Blake and some of his entourage, and since the man was a widower, she was seated directly on his right. There was no opportunity for other than casually inane conversation with him, though she found herself liking his open, friendly manner and she liked his looks as well.

In his early forties, Joel Blake, who had lost his mate far too early just as Ellen had, was unpretentious, though he carried an air of authority that he would need if he won the election. There were lines of character in his strong, craggy face, and his voice was pleasantly deep. A few streaks of gray were scattered through his thick, dark wavy hair, which gave him a distinguished look, and his height matched hers in her heels, so that when they stood together before they took their seats, his warm brown eyes were directly level with hers.

His speech was brief, witty, and charming, though his opening line had Ellen's cheeks glowing with a combination of embarrassment and pleasure.

"This is the sort of occasion I especially like," he started out in a droll tone. "I look out over the crowd and count heads, knowing exactly what each one of you paid to be here and mentally adding the amount to my campaign fund, and to top it off, I find I'm allowed to sit beside one of the loveliest women in the state." He glanced down at Ellen, his eyes teasing her warmly as the crowd applauded and laughed. Then he added, "Not only is she younger than I am and prettier to boot, but she's a first-rate fund-raiser as well. Ellen, stand up and take a bow and let some of the other gentlemen here envy me my good fortune in having such a lovely supporter."

Ellen did so, her complexion pinkening charmingly, then sat down again as hastily as she could, unused to and not particularly liking being the center of attention. At seeing her reaction, Joel Blake's appreciative gaze grew even warmer. "And she's modest and shy as well, folks," he quipped. "What more could a politician ask for?"

This remark was greeted with good-natured laughter, though Ellen, whose eyes had sought out Ross inadvertently, noted sourly that his expression denoted a great deal of scepticism at hearing her described as modest and shy, though she realized that, at least in her dealings with him, he had a good bit of justification for his doubts.

After the dinner, there was dancing, and Ellen was a little disconcerted when Joel Blake, rather than engaging in one duty dance with her, lingered on to claim her several times, a fact that brought a deeper and deeper scowl to Marcus's handsome features, and even a faint coldness into Ross's clear blue eyes as he watched them.

She herself was having almost a lovely time . . . except when she would catch sight of Ross and Freda dancing closely together, their gazes locked in smoldering glances that made Ellen's glance smolder a little, too, though with an entirely different emotion than the two of them were displaying.

However, it was impossible not to respond to Joel Blake's warm charm, nor to remain unflattered by his obvious increasing interest in her as a woman rather than as just another fund-raiser.

"Do you come to Topeka often?" he was asking now, pulling her imperceptibly closer and dropping his voice into a lower, more intimate register.

"Oh . . . ah . . . why, yes, at least twice a week," Ellen faltered, uncertain how to respond to his flirtatiousness.

Was he just taking an opportunity for some lighthearted relief from his grueling schedule, or was his interest genuine? She didn't know, but she wasn't left in doubt long.

"Good," he replied with satisfaction. "Will you have dinner with me the next time our schedules coincide?"

Ellen moved back from him slightly to blink up at him with candid inquiry. "Why?" she asked ingenuously.

He gave a delighted chuckle, his dark eyes warmly appreciative as he studied her inquiring face. "Why do you think, Ellen?" he teased her mischievously. "Don't you know how attractive you are? I am single now, you know, and so are you. And I think we might have a lot in common, and I like you, and you're beautiful and sexy and honest and . . ."

He stopped, studying Ellen's increasingly flushed face with sardonic interest. "Shall I go on, or should I save something for when we have that dinner?" he drawled mockingly.

"Oh, by all means, save something . . ." Ellen responded a little weakly, causing Joel to chuckle again.

"Then it's settled," he said smoothly, taking her words as acceptance of his invitation. "I'll give you a call when I have a free date and see if it's convenient for you, all right?"

Ellen merely nodded, feeling a little overwhelmed by his interest, yet pleased as well. She liked him, too, though she had no desire to share the life he lived. But, after all, he was only asking her for a date, not making a proposal, so why shouldn't she take the opportunity to spend some time in the company of a man she actually liked for a change?

He left soon after bestowing his invitation, and a very sulky Marcus Fielding reappeared to suggest they leave as well.

"Oh, I can't yet, Marcus," Ellen said straightfaced,

determined to put off the forthcoming wrestling match for as long as possible. "I have to see that everything goes smoothly for the rest of the evening. It's my job as one of the hostesses, remember?"

It was clear that Marcus preferred not to remember, but as he had little choice, he gave in with grudging resentment, while Ellen spent most of the rest of the evening inventing tasks to keep out of his way. By the time they were climbing into his Mercedes, which she suspected was rented to impress her, she was as tired and cranky as he was. Ross hadn't once come near her, much less asked her to dance.

At her door she turned her cheek to him, and Marcus said rather grimly, "I'd like to come in."

Whereupon Ellen responded equally grimly, "And I'd rather you didn't. I'm tired, Marcus. Let's call it an evening, all right?"

His rather cold blue eyes narrowed into slits, Marcus asked, "Just why did you call me and ask me to escort you tonight, Ellen? You'd turned down all my invitations after that one date we had, and tonight you acted as if I barely existed. What the hell are you playing at?"

Ellen sighed and fixed him with a steady look of complete disinterest. "The same thing you've been playing at for years, Marcus. I needed a pretty face, and you provided it." She grimaced at his look of outrage. "Come on, Marcus, don't act so injured. You know you would never have asked me out in the first place if you hadn't been more interested in my bank balance than in *my* pretty face. Can you deny it?" she questioned dryly at seeing the disconcerted look replace the outrage in his expression.

"Why, Ellen, how can you think such a thing?" He started to flounder out a protest and Ellen waved a hand at him dismissingly.

"Can it, Marcus. I don't need any explanations. I also

don't need any more of your time, so let's say good night and good-bye and let it go at that, hmmm?"

A dark flush of anger colored his handsome face, but Marcus dropped his role of pretense quickly. "That suits me fine," he snarled at her. "And you're right about your bank balance being more attractive than your face. I prefer blondes who know the score anyway!"

"Lovely," Ellen smiled at him sweetly. "Then go find yourself one and leave me in peace, okay?"

Marcus spluttered incoherently for a moment, then turned his broad shoulders away and stalked to his car while Ellen watched him go with prosaic amusement, hoping the rental on that car hadn't put him too much out of pocket, considering it had turned out to be a useless expense. But, then, he had gotten a free dinner, hadn't he? She had provided the tickets for the dinner.

With a dismissing shrug she turned to go in, feeling tired and discouraged that Ross had been so completely disinterested in her that evening and so damned attentive to the disgustingly lovely Freda! She took a long, hot bath, donned the beautiful black nightgown John had bought her a few weeks before his death, hoping she would lift her spirits a little by contemplating what Ross was missing, but failing abominably when she realized she was missing the same thing, and crawled into bed to drown her despondency in sleep.

Sometime later she was awakened by a determined ringing of her doorbell, and she dragged herself out of bed to stagger to the door, wondering what idiot had the rudeness to come pounding on someone's door in the middle of the night. She switched on the porch light, glared out the small windowpane in the door, then sucked in her breath when she saw Ross standing there.

Her hands trembling with nervousness, she undid the lock, swung open the door, then stepped hastily back out of the way when he strode in without so much as a word of greeting to take a few steps inside, then turned to glare down at her.

Ellen shut the door behind her, then stood with her back to it, drinking in the sight of him through her puzzled apprehension.

"Who is that jerk you were with tonight?" he demanded immediately, his gaze raking over her with a combination of possessiveness and anger.

"Marcus?" Ellen faltered.

"Marcus," Ross nodded, sneering the name. "How in the world could you go out with such a complete ass? Is that someone you would want John to know you found attractive?"

Bristling, Ellen stuck out her lower lip with stubborn sulkiness. "You don't even know him!" she snapped back, determined he wasn't going to find out she shared his opinion of Marcus completely. "And what makes you think John wouldn't approve of him? He was a lot more sensitive to people than you'll ever be!"

"Exactly!" Ross snarled back at her. "He would have known within one minute the man was a posturing hypocrite. It took me two!"

Clenching her fists in frustration, Ellen took a threatening step toward him, common sense rapidly leaving her in favor of retaliation. "Well, your Freda was no angelic picture of honesty either, you fink! What do you think John would have thought of her?!"

At this Ross relaxed slightly, giving her a pitying smile. "John would have been very much aware that it wasn't Freda's . . . ah . . . saintly qualities I was interested in," he drawled with a suggestive quirk of his eyebrow, and then he looked dangerously speculative before he relaxed again. "For a while there, considering that the only thing Marcus has going for him is a healthy male body, I wondered if you were interested in him for the same reasons I asked Freda out. But since he isn't here, I guess I misjudged you." He paused then, his gaze raking her black nightgown scathingly. "Or did I just get here too late to miss all the fun and games?"

A strangled sound of mingled outrage and hurt leaving her throat, Ellen launched herself at Ross, meaning to scratch his eyes out. He caught her uplifted hands easily, smiling with dangerous alertness as he forced them behind her back and held her against him with a grip of steel that made mincemeat of her efforts to struggle against him.

"You never learn, do you?" he muttered, his voice going husky as he imprisoned both of her wrists in one large paw and used his other hand to tilt her chin up to face him. "And this time you're giving me a lot more incentive to take up your challenge than you did in your fuzzy pink pajamas . . . or even a towel." His blue eyes flickered down over her black nightgown meaningfully, and the heat in them made Ellen catch her breath.

"Ross Sayer, don't you dare . . ." she started to protest feebly, but even as the last word came out, he was shutting off the sound with his mouth, and his warm, mobile lips caused such instant havoc to Ellen's senses that she wailed inwardly at how hard fate made it to maintain her pride and self-respect when it kept tossing someone like Ross into her path at every turn!

Then all thought was impossible as Ross deepened the kiss and she felt the taut hardness against her thighs that spelled out how much he wanted her. He held the kiss, pressing her lower body against him until he felt her body relax its tension and begin to melt into his, and then he released her hands so that he could caress her with his own.

"Ellen . . ." he murmured hoarsely against her lips, his

99

hands roaming feverishly over her. "God, I want you! I need you!"

Some perverseness made her draw back slightly, and she gazed into his eyes with solemn question. "Freda . . . ?" she asked, a world of meaning behind the one word.

Ross looked back at her, something like rueful disgust in his eyes. "I took her home immediately after the dance," he admitted. "All I could think of was you here with that ass, Marcus, and I didn't even kiss Freda good night. If I'd found him here, I think I would have killed him!"

Ellen smiled back at him with affectionate sheepishness. "I only went out with him because I was angry with you," she admitted in her turn. "He's so pretty, I thought it would give you the message that I have a Freda or two up my sleeve the same as you do."

One eyebrow cocked sardonically, Ross cupped her head in his hands, one thumb running deliciously over her mouth. "What are we doing, Ellen?" he asked quietly. "I want you so badly sometimes, it's all I can do to function."

Ellen held his gaze, her own soft and clear. "You know what we're doing, Ross," she said just as quietly. "You're waiting to stop wanting me because you don't want to get married, and I'm waiting to find someone who will make me stop wanting you."

He grasped her shoulders then, his expression faintly grim. "Ellen, if you only knew what Tina put me through . . ."

She shushed him, placing cool fingers over his mouth. "I know, Ross. Not the details, but the effect. And I'm sorry." She shrugged acceptingly. "But it doesn't change anything. You're still you . . . and I'm still me." There was sad resignation in her tone, and Ross almost winced at hearing it. Then he kissed her again, as though he wanted to shut out the barriers between them with the one thing they shared wholeheartedly.

Ellen responded, reveling in the feel of his mouth on hers, in the broad strength of his chest under her hands, and in the heat of his body pressed against hers. She wanted him so! And he wanted her! She could feel the evidence setting fire to her own loins.

One last time! she promised herself as he impatiently swung her up into his arms and started toward her bedroom. Just this one last time, she would allow herself to have what she desired so fiercely; she had no strength to combat that desire.

And a few minutes later, as Ross stood over her, nude and gloriously warm with the heat of his passion, a small, tiny voice inside her head echoed with gladness the thought that Ross was seeing her as she had wanted him to that morning so long ago on the ski trip. His hands ran over the black silk with delicious sensing, creating a heated response everywhere he touched, until finally he removed that last filmy barrier and touched the flesh beneath with an urgency Ellen met with every fibre of her being.

"Fast or slow, Ellen?" he growled at her as he lowered her to the bed and covered her body with his own. "Tell me what you want."

"Both!" she gasped, delighting in the sharp indrawn breath he took as she wriggled beneath him, accommodating herself to his form. "Oh, God, I don't care, Ross, so long as you love me at all!"

She didn't care that Ross probably took her words in a sexual rather than an emotional sense . . . not when she felt herself once again being drawn into that heated, mindlessly passionate vortex where she and Ross were inseparable on all levels. It was enough for the moment that she was the only one who loved in the truest, most complete

101

sense. There would be time enough in the morning to regret that another love of his had created the barrier he now apparently found it impossible to cross to this new love.

CHAPTER NINE

The next morning came all too soon, since Ross was a rancher whose days started before the sun put in an appearance. She made them coffee, which Ross drank without even seating himself at the table, but whether his impatience sprang from a desire to get to the ranch and start work, or whether he was simply anxious to get yet another good-bye between them over and done with, was something Ellen didn't know and didn't care to contemplate.

Finally, he placed his empty cup on the counter and faced her with a grim expression. "Ellen, I don't want this to end when I leave this morning. Have an affair with me!" he said gruffly, his very tone indicating how torn he was at making the suggestion.

Every emotional part of her wanted to say yes. But every ounce of common sense she possessed argued no. She raised troubled eyes to his, lifted one hand toward him uncertainly, then dropped it into her lap. He walked over to her, seated himself beside her, and took her other hand into both of his.

"Honey, if I thought it would work, I'd ask you to marry me," he said in a low, almost agonized voice. "You know that, don't you?"

Ellen studied him, her gaze loving, sad . . . and curious. "Ross," she ventured hesitantly, "what exactly did Tina do to you?" There was a helpless plea for enlightenment, for understanding, in her tone that finally wiped away the instantaneous closed look that came over his face and replaced it with a grimace of impatient reluctance to explain what she asked. Then he gave a deep sigh of accord and raked a hand through his thick hair.

"I guess you could say she destroyed my belief that one person can ever truly know another one," he said in a dry, remote, and somewhat angry tone. "When I married her, I thought she was every man's dream." He gave a grunt of disgust. "And that's exactly what she was really—a dream. There wasn't much substance to her at all, and what there was, well, let's just say it wasn't the kind of substance that does a man much good. She was totally self-involved."

Reluctant to let his less-than-detailed explanation end there, Ellen encouraged him to go on. "What did you want from her, Ross?" she asked gently.

"Honesty, for one thing," he clipped out, his gaze growing even more remote. "For instance, she led me to believe for six months that we were trying to have a baby." His eyes looked bleak, and Ellen ached for him. "Needless to say, it was something of a shock when I caught her taking birth control pills and learned she'd been doing so from the beginning." He shrugged, the movement oddly vulnerable. "At least it was a relief to know I wasn't sterile," he said in an ironic tone. "She had been making veiled references to the fact that I might be."

"Oh, Ross!" Ellen's indignant sympathy burst out of her, her eyes wide and eloquent with the same.

"And fidelity," he went on as though he hadn't heard. "She was having an affair with the man she left me for for quite some time before she got him to the point where he offered marriage."

Ellen gave a helpless little movement with her free

hand, longing to comfort him and uncertain how to do so. He didn't give her the chance, removing his hands from hers and getting to his feet in an abrupt movement.

"That ought to do for starters," he said, looking down at her with a grim little twist of a smile. "And don't bother telling me you aren't like Tina," he added as he saw just that thought in Ellen's wide, clear eyes. "With my head, I know you're not. I even know it with my heart. But part of me somewhere . . . somehow . . . is afraid."

He stopped, then shrugged as though explanations were useless. Ellen sat back and watched him, her expression indicative of the thoughts that tore through her—that Ross was being unfair to her, that while she understood his fear, she felt it grossly unwarranted in her case. And further, that it was beyond her to plead her own case when it was so apparent she would merely be dragging her pride in the dust, since his mind was closed already.

"Ellen, I'm sorry," and Ross's low tone said clearly that he meant it. "I've been burned. It doesn't matter that logic tells me I wouldn't be again with you. Logic doesn't seem to have much to do with it."

Ellen nodded bleakly, understanding what he meant. "It's all right, Ross," she said with soft acceptance. "I understand. But since my experiences with John were completely different, you have to understand that I'm not afraid of marrying again. I don't expect perfection from a husband. John wasn't perfect himself. But I do expect a life shared to be better than one spent alone." She got up from her chair and turned her back to him to rinse her cup at the sink. "An affair wouldn't solve anything, Ross," she said very quietly, knowing her words to be true. "So I think it's best if we say good-bye for good this time. I'm sorry too."

She didn't turn to look at him. She didn't want him to see the tears forming in her eyes against her will—tears of

105

frustration and anger and longing that couldn't be assuaged. She felt his stillness for a long moment, heard his murmured, deeply intoned, "So be it," and then his gentle, "Good-bye, Ellen," before he turned on his heel and left the room.

Ellen held rigidly onto her control until she heard the front door open and close, then let her stiff features crumple to reflect how heartsick she felt while the tears slowly rolled down her cheeks.

"Damn you, Tina!" she burst out on a hiccuping sob, wishing the woman were there right then so she could throw the dripping washcloth in her hand straight into that delicate heart-shaped face. "Why didn't you find your rich foreigner first instead of dripping your poison into my sweet Ross!"

She was almost tempted to run after Ross and agree to an affair simply in the hope that she could show him how wrong he was to let Tina spoil his faith in women in general. But she knew if she did, and then later Ross didn't come to love her, she would be as devastated as she had been when John died. She didn't feel brave enough to sustain two such losses, though she felt like a coward at admitting such a thing. More to the point, she felt like a traitor for not having the courage to go that extra step for Ross when it might mean he would spend the rest of his life alone . . . childless . . . wrapped in an increasing bitterness that would spoil the years ahead of him.

Ellen swung around to go to her bedroom, muttering self-defensively, "Well, he's a big boy, smarter than most. If he can't figure out what he's missing on his own, he's not likely to find it out from me!"

But when she got to the bedroom and faced the crumpled bed where she had known such ecstasy the night before she gave a little whimper of unhappiness and crawled back in among the disorder to clutch the pillow where Ross had lain his head against her breast while she rocked back and forth crying out her misery until exhaustion brought her the welcome relief of sleep.

When she woke again, it was mid-morning, and she felt groggy, cross, and as tired as if she hadn't slept at all. A hot shower helped, but the face that stared back at her from the mirror as she brushed her hair still bore traces of a dangerously foul mood, and when the phone rang a few moments later, her tone would have done justice to a grizzly wakened from a sound winter's hibernation.

"Hello!" she snarled.

There was a slight pause, and then Ross said very gently, "Did I mention when we talked this morning that I'm in love with you?"

It was Ellen's turn to pause then, and perhaps her tiredness and her mental state combined to give her the equilibrium to answer calmly. "No, you didn't, and I guess I didn't say it either, but I do too." Then realizing that hadn't come out right, she added, "Love you, I mean. I love you, too, Ross."

"That's good to know, honey," he said quietly. "Maybe someday . . ." He didn't finish, and Ellen was in no mood to contemplate "someday" when she needed him *now*!

"Fiddlesticks!" she said crossly. "I haven't got time to wait for *someday*, Ross Sayer! I want you now, and I want your babies now, and, furthermore, I want to live on your ranch with you now! You mark my words, you'll be sorry *someday* when you find out what you've passed up! Meanwhile, I'm going to follow that old Biblical injunction about there being a time to do everything. It's time I got married again and started a family and that's exactly what I'm going to do! So, so long, Ross Sayer. See you around . . . *someday*!"

She banged the phone down before he could reply, grabbed up her purse, and departed from the house to

107

drive to a place in the country where she could walk off her temper without fear of being disturbed. But when she was able to think coherently again, all she could wonder was just *who* she was going to find to marry and father her children and replace Ross Sayer in her heart.

CHAPTER TEN

Joel Blake followed up on his promise to call her and fix a date to have dinner, and by the time he did so, Ellen would have accepted an invitation from Attila the Hun, much less a charming, attractive man she already liked. It had been a very stormy, sulky, miserable week since her last conversation with Ross, and she was thoroughly sick of herself and her immediate surroundings.

"I'm sorry I can't come and pick you up, Ellen," Joel said with real regret. "But my schedule now is such that it's impossible. Will you forgive me?"

Thinking that she would have forgiven him much more than that, Ellen replied cheerfully, "Only if you promise to buy me the biggest steak in Kansas. I warn you, I have a hearty appetite."

He chuckled. "Good for you," he said appreciatively. "And I do promise. In fact, I'm looking forward to seeing you again so much, I may bring the whole steer if it will make you happy."

Pleased and flattered, Ellen demurred with a laugh. "For heaven's sake, I said I have a healthy appetite, not that I'm a complete glutton! One steak will do, thank you very much!"

"One steak it is then," Joel said promptly. "I'll see you Thursday night, Ellen."

When they rang off, Ellen contemplated the phone

thoughtfully, aware that she felt better than she had in days, but still unable to quell the stubborn, fruitless wish that it was Ross she would be seeing next Thursday night instead of Joel Blake, though she knew a lot of women would have given almost anything to be in her shoes. Joel was an exciting man, and it was a shame she couldn't view their date with a lot more enthusiasm than she was able to muster at the moment.

However, as she drove to Topeka the next Thursday, her mood had lightened and she was almost grimly determined to enjoy herself if it killed her! Fortunately, it didn't come to that. Joel made the evening a delight from the moment she joined him at his campaign headquarters until shortly before the evening was at an end.

His store of wit kept her laughing, his admiring glances salved her ego, and his interesting conversation sparked her mind into high gear. On top of that, the steak he'd promised and provided was mouthwatering.

As they came out of the small, secluded restaurant where he had been recognized yet granted the peace and privacy they both desired, she was thinking it had been a delightful evening and that Joel Blake was altogether a delightful man. She felt a little nervous when he scooted over close to her in the back seat of the limousine that was taking them back to her car, but not unduly so. She knew he was going to kiss her, and she was actually hoping she would find his kiss as delightful as the rest of him.

He put an arm over her shoulders and pulled her against him, and she looked up at him, nervously expectant, then watched as his firm, nicely formed mouth came closer and closer until it rested gently against hers. The kiss was explorative at first, and Ellen gradually relaxed into it, finding it pleasant if not earth-shattering, the way Ross's kisses were, until she felt confident enough to return the stroking movement Joel offered.

110

At feeling her response, Joel deepened the kiss slightly, testing with his tongue to see if she was going to allow him entry into the sweet recesses of her mouth. Ellen pondered for an instant, then decided, why not? It was nice to feel his growing need for her, though she fully intended to stop things before they went too far. It was much too soon to encourage him to expect more than she was capable of giving as yet.

But she wasn't quite prepared for the mastery with which he took over! Suddenly, his need was not just growing—it had erupted full-blown, and Ellen was gasping for breath a few seconds later under the onslaught of his very male, very skilled, lovemaking!

"Joel!" she protested weakly when at last his ravaging mouth had left her own to travel to the sensitive skin of her neck. "Please!"

He lifted his head, his brown eyes liquid with passion, a small, taut twist quirking his lips. "Will you come home with me, Ellen?" he whispered in husky, grating tones. "I want you. I haven't wanted a woman like this since . . ."

Beneath her alarm at how quickly he had taken fire, Ellen knew he was thinking about his wife, and she knew a moment of consideration for him, having been through just the sort of loneliness she could hear in his voice. Therefore, her reply was delivered gently.

"Joel, no . . . please. We don't even know each other yet. It's much too soon for . . ." She shrugged helplessly, not wanting to spell things out bluntly.

He rested his forehead against her, and there was rueful self-amusement when he replied. "Not for me," he said wryly. "I am one aching, wanting man at this moment, though I suppose I can rake up the self-control to get hold of myself if you insist."

Ellen smiled her reply at him, letting him know that

111

though she didn't intend to change her mind, she didn't feel offended by his need for her. And as the limousine slid to a stop near her car, Joel straightened, releasing her, a ruefully resigned look on his attractive face.

"All right, Ellen," he said with a slightly shaky laugh. "I suppose I did jump the gun a little. Believe me, I didn't intend to, but you felt so good." He shrugged and gave her a lopsided, charming grin. "I took myself by surprise as much as I must have you."

"It's all right, Joel," she said quietly, reaching out to pat his knee affectionately. "I know what it's like to be lonely."

"Do you?" he asked almost bleakly, then sighed. "Yes, I suppose you must. It's hell losing the one person who makes it all mean something, isn't it?" Then, upon seeing her understanding, sympathetic nod, he smiled gratefully at her. "I hope I haven't spoiled whatever chance I had to see if you and I can find an answer to that loneliness together?" he asked with soft hopefulness.

"No, Joel," Ellen answered after a moment of thoughtful silence. "I do like you. I—I have to tell you though that I'm emotionally involved with someone else right now, though it doesn't look as though it will ever work out."

She must have sounded as unhappy as she felt at thinking of Ross, for Joel frowned down at her, his expression one of concern and perhaps a tiny bit jealous. "Oh," he said flatly, disappointment in his tone. But then, ever the optimist, he smiled at her. "I'm sorry if you're hurting, Ellen, but, though candor isn't supposed to be a politician's forte, I have to confess I'm glad to be offered some hope that I'm not completely out of the running."

Ellen gazed at him, a little startled at the rapidity with which he was pressing his suit. And as much as she liked him and enjoyed his company, as much as he was a welcome relief to the other men she'd dated recently, his reminder that he was a politician and led a life she felt unprepared to embrace wholeheartedly made her wonder about the wisdom of encouraging him to pursue his suit.

"I . . . ah . . . Joel." She stumbled for words to express her doubts and failed.

"Don't worry about it right now, Ellen," he said with confident gentleness. "If we find we really have anything going for us, I think all your doubts will melt away." Then he helped her on with her light stole. "Right now I think you'd better get on your way home. It's a long drive at night, and I hate it that you have to make it alone. This life has some penalties as well as rewards," he said somewhat grimly, though Ellen knew he was dedicated to seeking the opportunity to put his political ideals into practice.

They climbed out of the back of the limousine and Joel walked her to her car. When they reached it, he turned her to face him, his hands on her shoulders. "May I kiss you good night, Ellen?" he asked with humorous self-mockery. "I promise it will be just a kiss this time."

Ellen smiled up at him, liking him more all the time. "Yes, Joel," she said simply. "I'd like that."

He folded her into his arms, and while the kiss was restrained, Ellen was left in no doubt that Joel was having to work to keep it so. He was just withdrawing from her when she heard a scurrying sound and then light exploded in her face with blinding intensity, making her blink and jerk back in astounded perplexity.

"How about another one, Mr. Blake?" a cheerful voice called out, disregarding the now ferocious look on Joel Blake's face. "And how about an interview? Who's the lovely lady, sir?"

It dawned on Ellen then that the ever vigilant press had tracked them down, and she was grateful when Joel shielded her with his body, reaching down at the same time to jerk the door of her car open. "Get in and get going, Ellen," he said grimly. "I'm sorry about this, but it goes with the territory. If we want any privacy from here on out, however, let's keep your identity a secret for as long as we can."

Ellen nodded gratefully, slipping into the driver's seat of the car and inserting her key into the ignition as quickly as she could manage. "I'll call you," Joel promised, as he shut the door on her when the engine caught. Then he turned back to the members of the press who were starting to crowd around, forcing a tight smile.

"Good evening, ladies . . . gentlemen," Ellen heard him say as she quickly put the car in gear and pulled away. She was half afraid someone would follow her, but it seemed the press was content to settle for their more exciting prey, and as she glanced anxiously back in her rearview mirror, she saw that Joel was now surrounded and was holding court with a tight rein on the temper she had glimpsed so briefly a moment before.

"Oh, well," she consoled herself as she drove with sure swiftness toward home. "What did you expect, ninny? You weren't out with the Invisible Man after all."

Still, however, it was an unsettling taste of what continuing to date Joel Blake might entail, and as much as she liked and admired him, Ellen was not at all sure she was prepared to engage in a courtship subject to scrutiny by an entire state's avidly interested citizens.

The next day, and the next, she spent working in the bookstore, as it was the end of the month and there was paperwork to be done, so that by Sunday she was glad to have a chance just to put her feet up and enjoy a peaceful day of reading the paper, followed perhaps by some puttering in the garden. She had just settled herself on the couch with a cup of coffee and the voluminous Sunday paper when the telephone rang, and upon answering it,

Ellen was subjected to an excited burst of unintelligible gibberish from Rosie.

"Rosie, will you calm down and speak slowly so I can understand you?" Ellen asked with some puzzlement. All she had been able to get out of Rosie's spate was the name, Joel Blake.

"You sly devil!" Rosie chortled in reply. "Why didn't you tell me you and our prospective governor were dating!?"

Ellen rolled her eyes to the ceiling and shrugged, though Rosie couldn't see that. "I've had *one* date with the man, Rosie. I don't think that constitutes dating." Then she frowned. "How did you know about it?" she asked with some spirit. "Not that it's a secret," she added hastily, "but I haven't seen you to tell you about it, if I remember."

"A *secret*!" Rosie practically howled. "I'll say it's not a secret! Haven't you seen the society page of today's paper yet?"

Ellen froze, remembering the reporters the preceding Thursday night, then grimaced. "No, I haven't gotten that far yet, Rosie," she said somewhat crossly. "What does it say?"

"It would be more to the point to ask what *doesn't* it say," Rosie came back exuberantly. "And that picture! God, what a clinch!"

Ellen paled slightly. "Picture?" she asked in a faint voice.

"In full color," Rosie supplied, practically smacking her lips in remembrance. "That Joel Blake is a handsome devil, isn't he? Does he kiss as good as he looks?"

"Oh, God!" Ellen moaned, ignoring the question. "What a hassle! I thought Joel would do something to get them off the track!"

"Are you kidding?" Rosie laughed. "I doubt if any

115

reporter would squelch something as juicy as that about a current candidate, even if he or she was offered substantial blackmail."

Ellen muttered an unladylike expletive and scowled at the phone when her response just made Rosie laugh harder. "It's not funny, Rosie!" she upbraided her friend crossly. "I don't want my personal life paraded in front of anyone who cares to look."

"You should have thought of that before you agreed to go out with a man like Joel Blake," Rosie said with complacency. "Anyway, hon, I think it's great. And if you and Joel become an item, you might as well get used to it anyway. He lives in a fishbowl, you know, and so does everyone closely connected to him. How'd you like him, by the way?" she asked with avid curiosity. "Are you seriously interested in him?"

Ellen sighed in resignation. "I don't even know him that well, Rosie," she said dryly. "I like him, yes, but it's much too soon to get *interested,* as you call it."

"Well, I just hope you don't send him packing before you do get to know him," Rosie said sternly, "the way you've done every other man you've dated recently. You aren't likely to find another John, you know, but that doesn't mean you can't be happy with someone else, and Joel Blake seems like a dandy person. Give him a chance, why don't you?"

"Oh, I plan to," Ellen said abstractedly, wanting to end the conversation so she could get to the paper and see what had excited Rosie so much. "But don't make a mountain out of a molehill, Rosie. One date does not a relationship make."

"No, but it's a start," Rosie said firmly. "I thought for a while that you and R—" She bit off what she'd been about to say, though Ellen knew with a sinking feeling what it was she had on her mind. "Well, never mind, honey. I guess I was wrong." Rosie ducked the subject hastily. "You want to come over for dinner tonight?" She changed direction entirely then.

"Ah, er, no . . . thanks anyway, Rosie," Ellen demurred, "but I'm in the mood for a quiet day. But we'll get together sometime next week, okay?"

"Okay," Rosie agreed blithely, then gave a sly chuckle. "Now I'll hang up so you can get to the paper. I know you're dying to see what I'm talking about, aren't you?"

"Yes . . . dying . . ." Ellen said wryly, sticking her tongue out affectionately at the instrument in her hand as a substitute for Rosie.

"See you soon then." Rosie rang off with another laugh, and Ellen murmured a reply before banging the phone down to run to the couch and snatch up the paper.

She groaned audibly when she found the right section and the first thing that greeted her eyes was a large picture of Joel Blake kissing her as they stood by the car. The caption beneath brought another groan. In large block letters, it read, WIDOWER CANDIDATE FINDS SOLACE IN THE ARMS OF AVID SUPPORTER. WILL WEDDING BELLS RING SOON FOR POSSIBLE NEW GOVERNOR?

As if that weren't bad enough, the accompanying article practically spelled out her life history, leaving her astonished at how the press could have learned not only her name, but almost every detail of her life! There was a great deal of speculation about how serious Joel Blake was about her, as well, and Ellen read his quotes with a rising temper. He had never spelled out the fact that this was their first date, never directly denied that he was seriously interested in her, and had left the overall impression that they were a lot more involved than they were.

"Never trust a politician," Ellen murmured angrily to herself. "And he was the one who had said we should keep our relationship quiet for a while too!"

117

It took quite a while for her to settle down enough to really think about why she was so angry, and when she did, she was puzzled by her own reaction. After all, what difference did it make if the whole world thought she and Joel Blake were an item?

The whole world . . . She thought about that and finally zeroed in on why she was really so concerned. She didn't give a flip about what the whole world knew or didn't know. It was Ross Sayer's knowing she couldn't take!

"That's silly!" she remonstrated with herself as she pounded a pillow on her bed within an inch of its life in the process of straightening it up. She was, as usual, using physical activity to work off the anxiety of turbulent thoughts. "I ought to be glad Ross knows I'm not sitting around on my tail waiting for *someday*!"

But she wasn't glad. She was worried, though just why she should be escaped her. She and Ross had made no commitments. She didn't have to account to him for her actions. As things stood now, they were finished, each proceeding with his or her own life without thought for the other. She had even told him she was going to find someone else, though she had been having a temper tantrum at the time.

So why did she have this awful foreboding that that article in the paper was merely a prelude to something far more drastic? It was a dumb way to feel, she assured herself crossly. Ross was a civilized man, after all, and what's more, he probably wouldn't even care whether there were wedding bells in her and Joel Blake's future. If he had, he would have done something before now to ensure she didn't marry anyone but him!

Her assurances to herself rang somewhat hollow, but since they were all she had, she clung to them and marched into the kitchen to fix a bologna and cheese sandwich to fill the empty space that had developed some-where in the region of her stomach.

She had just taken a huge, ferocious chomp off the sandwich when the phone began to ring again, and she glared at the receiver on the wall as though it were person-ally responsible for her foul mood.

"Hello!" she mumbled around the bite in her mouth.

"Ellen?" Joel Blake's smooth, pleasant voice echoed in her ear in a puzzled tone. "Is that you?"

Swallowing the half-chewed bite with a gulp that almost strangled her, Ellen choked out. "Yes, it's me, and I'm glad you called, Joel Blake! I want you to know I don't appreciate one bit being displayed to all and sundry in a . . . a compromising position!"

Joel's answering chuckle infuriated her, but before she could express her fury, he broke in. "Now, Ellen, I hardly think you could call a harmless kiss being compromised. What a way to describe it anyway. It sounds like some-thing from the Victorian Age!"

"Nevertheless—" Ellen sputtered, incensed at his cal-lous disregard of her concern, but he cut her off.

"I know, I know, Ellen," he soothed. "I called to you I'm sorry it happened."

"Just how *did* it happen?" Ellen asked with cross sus cion in her voice. "I thought you were going to keep anonymous, but here I am plastered over the paper li celebrity, and your quotes didn't help matters eithe

"Honey, once they're on the trail, there's not anyone can do about it," Joel sighed; his patience with her inexperience where such matters were concerned was limited. "I expect one of them took down your license number when you drove away, I don't know. And as for my quotes—" He paused and Ellen impatiently broke in.

"Yes, what about them?" she challenged sternly.

"Well, to tell you the truth, I made them for your

119

benefit," Joel said, sounding somewhat sheepish. "I didn't want you to think I wouldn't acknowledge you. Since the cat was out of the bag anyway . . ."

"What?" Ellen yelped in astonishment, flabbergasted by his explanation. "What cat? What bag? Joel!" she practically wailed. "We've had only one date, for heaven's sake!"

"Now, Ellen," he came back, his voice as smooth and calming as velvet. "You know it isn't going to stop with one date, don't you? Damn it, I *am* interested! And that's really all I said, wasn't it?" he asked coaxingly.

Thinking back, Ellen realized he was right, but she remained unmollified because she knew how that article would sound to anybody who read it, especially Ross Sayer!

"Joel . . ." she started to say, her voice holding a warning threat.

"Oh, I know, honey," he said calmly. "You don't like publicity. At least you don't now. But it's like anything else. A person can get used to anything if they want to. Not that I'm saying it has to be like this all the time," he added hastily when he heard her begin to sputter again. "Just that it's not really such a big deal. I'll be more careful next time, and make sure the press doesn't horn in on any more of our dates."

Stumped by his persistence, Ellen remained silent, trying to thrash out whether she wanted to see him again or end it now. Joel did all he could to aid her decision in his favor.

"I enjoyed our date enormously, Ellen," he said in a low, intimate voice. "And I want to repeat it as soon as possible. Will you forgive me for what happened and at least agree to see me again soon?"

"Well . . ." Ellen wavered, touched by the note of pleading in his tone. She did like him, darn it! she thought to herself frustratedly. And she admired him. She just didn't particularly want to be involved in a life that resembled a goldfish bowl.

"Come on, sweetheart," he coaxed charmingly. "Say yes. In fact, say you'll come to dinner with me next Sunday night. A friend of mine has a place out in the country where we can be alone, and I'll cook your dinner myself. A big, fat, juicy steak, baked potato, salad, chocolate cake and ice cream for dessert!"

Ellen looked down at the remains of her bologna sandwich, now looking slightly the worse for wear from having been clenched in her fist all the time she was talking, and an involuntary grin stretched her mouth. "Have you got spies watching me?" she asked with a dry chuckle. "I was just having a bologna sandwich."

"See?" Joel quipped without missing a beat. "You need someone to take care of you and make sure you eat properly. And I'm just the man to do it. I cook a mean steak, baby!" he drawled suggestively, and Ellen could almost see him wiggling his eyebrows.

"Why do I get the feeling it's your hand you want me to eat out of it instead of a plate?" she drawled back at him wryly.

"Who, me?" he said with injured innocence. And then he laughed, his voice deep and confident and masculine. "I'm prepared to offer you both, babe," he admitted. "It's up to you to choose which one you want. I promise I'll be a perfect gentleman." And there was a note of sincerity in his voice Ellen trusted.

"All right," she gave in, making her voice sulkily grudging. "But if I see so much as a Brownie Instamatic on the place, you're in for trouble, buster!"

Joel laughed, and it was a most pleasant sound. "Scout's honor, Ellen," he promised with mock gravity. "It'll be just you and me, babe."

Ellen smiled, in harmony with him again, and was about to open her mouth to make some retort when she looked up to see Ross Sayer glaring in at her through the window on the back door. Instantly, her composure fled and it was all she could do to keep her voice calm as she rang off.

"Fine, Joel," she murmured absently. "I have to go now, okay?"

"Okay," he responded with a soft note of intimacy. "I'll be counting the hours until Sunday, Ellen."

"Uh, yes, well, all right," Ellen said, jumping as Ross gave a thumping crash of a knock on the door, impatient anger etched into his face like granite. "Bye, Joel," she said hastily and barely heard his answering farewell before she was practically throwing the phone back on its hook.

She threw the sandwich down on the table and crossed to the door to swing it open just as Ross was lifting his fist to give it another thwack, and the two of them stood glaring at each other for an instant before both spoke at once.

"Who were you talking to?" Ross snarled.

"Why did you come to the back door?" Ellen snapped.

The two of them paused, then both answered at once.

"Joel Blake!" Ellen hurled at Ross defiantly.

"Because you didn't answer the knock on the front door!" Ross gritted sarcastically.

Both fell silent then, Ross eyeing Ellen with growing animosity, Ellen eyeing Ross with growing wariness. "Won't you come in?" she asked with strained politeness, the strain coming from the fact that Ross was already brushing past her to enter the house without benefit of invitation.

Ellen carefully shut the door behind him, then swung around to face him, her face set in lines of stony unwel-

122

come. Ross faced her, his face stonily unyielding, his fists on his hips, his stance dangerous.

"You sure as hell didn't wait long, did you?" he attacked gratingly.

"I never promised I'd wait at all," Ellen replied with more bravery than she felt, wondering inwardly why she was pursuing the insane course of provoking Ross further than he already was and not coming up with an answer that made the least sense. He was patently on the verge of strangling her within an inch of her life, and all she could do was encourage him to do just that.

"What are you trying to do to me?" he snarled.

"I'm not trying to do anything to you, Ross Sayer!" Ellen snapped. "I'm just trying to live my life the best I can. You don't want to live it with me, so why should you care if I . . ."

She broke off, taking one wary step backward as Ross took two threatening steps forward. "Don't you touch me!" she warned quaveringly. "You have no right to come in here like an enraged bull and . . ."

She should have kept her mouth shut, Ellen realized with alarm an instant later when Ross took that last step and caught her shoulders in a bruising grip.

"I'd like to throttle you!" he grated in a tone of fury, his ice blue eyes blazing fire at her. "But it's too damned hard to live without you, so I'm going to marry you instead! You get yourself ready, lady, because three days from now I'm going to have you permanently under my nose where you'd better think twice before you get plastered all over the newspaper kissing some other man!"

"Wh . . . how . . . Ross!" Ellen squeaked just before he brought his mouth down in a crashing kiss that stunned her with its ferocity. She didn't know whether he meant it as a gesture to seal his proposal or as sheer punishment, but it held no pleasure for her.

123

"Stop it, you brute!" she snarled at him when he finally raised his head to glare at her again. "That hurt!"

"I hope so!" he snarled back at her. "You deserve it!"

"I don't either!" she yelled, jerking back defensively when he would have sealed her mouth with another kiss. "Now, stop that, sit down, and talk to me like a civilized human being instead of a Neanderthal man!"

The two of them glared at each other for another few seconds before Ross thrust her away, stomped to the table, and seated himself with arms folded across his chest, his face as unyielding as stone.

Ellen took a deep breath, fumbled ineffectually with her blouse, trying to tuck it in more from a need to have something to do with her nervous hands than because it slipped from her jeans, then seated herself across from him, folding her hands demurely in front of her while she eyed him cautiously.

"Now, what were you saying?" she asked almost primly.

"You heard me!" he growled back at her. "We're getting married!"

"My, you certainly sport a pretty line in proposals," Ellen shot back grimly, then hastily backed off when she saw that dangerous look appear in Ross's blue eyes again. "All right, all right!" she protested, holding her hands up in defense. "What I meant to say was . . . well . . ." She looked at him nervously, then gained courage. "Why?" she said more firmly. "You don't want to get married again."

"Correction," Ross said grimly. "I *didn't* want to get married again. Now I've decided it's the only way I'm ever going to get through a day in one piece again." He fixed her with a glinting eye. "It's what you wanted, isn't it? What's the matter, are you having second thoughts now

124

that you're the apple of Joel Blake's eye?" The grating sarcasm in his voice made Ellen scowl back at him.

"Let's leave Joel Blake out of this!" she responded tartly. "It's *our* marriage we're talking about, and I want to know why you're suddenly doing an about-face on the subject. Is it just sheer male territorial right that prompted this charming proposal?"

To her disgruntled surprise, Ross looked speculatively thoughtful for a moment, then nodded his head. "Maybe so," he shrugged, looking as though it didn't matter one way or the other. Then he gazed back at her purposefully. "Who cares? The thing is, I'm hooked, and I'm in a hurry. I'm not about to let you flit off with that damned politician again! Now, it takes three days in this state to . . ."

Ellen cut him off, her tone indignant. "Now, just a minute, Ross Sayer! I haven't said I'll do it yet!"

Ross leaned forward, holding her with a ferocious look. "Don't you play games with me, Ellen," he threatened gratingly. "You love me, you want to marry me, and"— and here he eyed her with a look softening into something approaching amusement—"if I remember correctly, you want to have my babies *now,* and you want to live on my ranch with me *now,*" he quoted her with smug taunting. He cocked an inquiring, infuriatingly attractive eyebrow at her, and asked, "Haven't changed your mind, have you?"

Ellen huffed, crossing her arms against the urge to smack him a good one! "No, I haven't," she gritted hatefully. "But I don't want to be accused of entrapment the first time we have a fight either! I didn't go out with Joel Blake to bring you to heel, Ross. I went out with him to . . ."

She let the words die as she saw the look of danger spring up in his eyes again, causing her to recover her cautious sense of self-preservation. "Well, never mind."

125

She changed direction rapidly. "The thing is, I don't want to *dragoon* a husband with a shotgun. I want a man who's willing." She sat back and faced him sternly, waiting for whatever might come.

"Oh, I'm willing," he said with soft, implacable intent. "I'm not only willing, I'm determined." He sounded as immovable as a rock, and Ellen began to take him very seriously indeed. "But we're going to agree on a few rules first," he affirmed with a determined gleam in his eyes that made her extremely nervous.

"Ah . . . er . . . what sort of rules?" she asked with hesitant wariness, eyeing him suspiciously.

Ross held up his two powerful hands and began to enumerate. "One," he started off grimly, "I'll make the living in this family. You can put your money in a trust fund for our kids or whatever, but I don't want it shoved down my throat!" His hard look stifled her immediate protest as he held up another finger and continued. "Two, you're going to be busy on the ranch, so the bookstore work ceases the day we're married." At that, Ellen eyed him resentfully, though she felt an immediate lightening of the heart as though some burden had been lifted from her. Never able to thrust off John's legacy on her own, she was much relieved to be able to do it under Ross's direction, though she had no intention of telling him that. He was entirely too much of a bully already. She would have her work cut out for her teaching him the value of compromise in a relationship, she thought happily, unconsciously accepting that they were going to be married.

"Three," Ross continued determinedly, "I want strict honesty between us. If you have a headache and don't want my loving at bedtime, then for God's sake, say so! There may be a time or two when *I* don't feel like performing under the sheets either!" His frown lightened temporarily as he muttered half-teasingly, "Though I can't

126

imagine that happening for the time being." Then he was back to business, and his levity was totally erased. "And four, Ellen Bowman, soon to be Ellen Sayer, don't let me ever catch you so much as flirting with another man, or God help me, I don't know what I'll do. My tolerance on that subject is absolutely nil!"

Ellen faced his warning with calm, absolutely confident that she would never have to find out what it was he would or would not do under such circumstances. Then, without agreeing to his terms, she made some demands of her own.

"Is it my turn now?" she inquired politely when several seconds had gone by, during which Ross watched her with hawklike precision.

He sat back, eyeing her speculatively, then his features relaxed somewhat and he nodded his head with gracious patience.

"Good," Ellen said, her tone only mildly dry. "One"— she mocked his tone—"I don't ever want it thrown in my face that I coerced you into marrying me." She waited while Ross first grinned, then lifted his shoulders in a nonchalant shrug and nodded. "Two," she continued, "I don't want to be compared with, condemned for, or accused of being anything like Tina. I am not like her, and I have no intention of suffering for her sins." Her stern tone made Ross smile, and he half-lowered his eyelids in agreement. "Three," she went on, satisfied that what she saw in his face was a sincere intention to see her as she was and not as Tina had been, "I don't believe in divorce, so you'd better be very sure this is what you want, Ross. There are very few things that would make me leave you, chief of which is infidelity." She bore the storm of his instantaneous scowl of injured dignity calmly, waited until she heard his muttered "Damn right!" and finished.

"And four, Ross," she said with a soft smile of an-

127

ticipated joy, "I want a baby right away. We're not getting any younger and . . ."

She got no further as Ross came up out of his seat and jerked her up into his arms with a power that took her breath away. "You've got it!" he said in a husky, emotion-laden voice that thrilled her to her soul. "Now, let's cut out the damned conditions and get down to what really matters!"

He kissed her then, his mouth enveloping hers, his tongue possessing her with every bit as much passion and loving anticipation as she could have wished for. Their bargain was sealed. She was dizzy by the time he raised his head, wanting him with every cell in her body. He smiled down at her, obviously enjoying her arousal as much as she was. "I want you too," he murmured seductively, "but we've got too much to do to while away the afternoon in the sack." He laughed as he saw her pout of disappointment.

"Such as?" she demanded sulkily. "I thought you said we were going to get down to what's really important!"

"And so we are, my impatient, lustful wife-to-be," he teased her as he pushed her away and turned her toward the living room, giving her a smack on her pert bottom. "And what's really important is getting us hitched. So we're going over to Rosie and Jake's to get things started."

Ellen shot him a look of dismay over her shoulder. "Oh, God!" she wailed. "Rosie will kill me. She had me lined up with Joel Blake for sure only two hours ago!"

Ross's blue eyes became hooded, though he was smiling. "Don't you believe it," he drawled with maddening confidence. "Rosie's known which way the wind was blowing long before either of us did. You're not the only one who's been trying to drag poor little old defenseless me to the altar for weeks now!"

Ellen stopped short, swinging to face Ross with fire in

her eye. "Ross, damn it, you promised you wouldn't
. . ."

"Tut, tut!" he mocked her, swooping down to graze a
kiss on her pursed lips. "I hope I'm not making the mistake of marrying *another* woman without a sense of humor." He gleefully broke condition number two of their
just completed bargain. "If so, I may have to look up
Freda every time you get on my case," he added, breaking
condition number three insouciantly, at least in spirit,
before he finished by coming very close to breaking condition number four. "And on second thought, I don't know
if I want a determined husband-chasing, humorless, narrowminded woman to be the mother of my children.
Maybe we'd better wait awhile before we . . ."

He barely had time to laughingly defend himself against
Ellen's howling, outraged body as she flung herself at him,
intending to make him pay dearly for his own misplaced
humor. The resulting scuffle was short and ended very
sweetly with a kiss that left them both doubtful as to
whether they needed to go see Rosie and Jake quite as
soon as Ross had intended.

"An hour or so shouldn't matter," Ross murmured
huskily against Ellen's lips as he stroked her with greedy
hands.

"An hour or so won't do it," Ellen murmured just as
huskily, her eyes slumberously teasing as she gazed lovingly at him from beneath her lashes. "I'm much too hungry
to settle for a snack."

"In that case," Ross grinned crookedly at her, "we'd
better go now or we'll never even get to our own wedding.
Besides," he teased her further as he released her very
reluctantly, "one of my men is off today, and I've got to
get back to the ranch once we've set things in motion."

"Ross!" Ellen wailed disappointedly, whereupon he
laughed outright.

"You're going to have to learn that on a ranch, the cows come first," he finally managed with solemn gravity. "Wives come second." And when Ellen glared her dislike of that particular sentiment, he conceded with gracious generosity. "However, if you'd like to come home with me tonight, I might be able to spare you a little time between two and four in the morning."

Ellen's eyes gleamed with anticipation and seductive challenge. "Oh, good," she said demurely. "I'll try to stay awake in case you can."

"You'll stay awake, all right," Ross growled at her meaningfully as he ushered her determinedly out the front door. "That's another thing a rancher's wife has to get used to—very little sleep."

"I'll do my duty then." Ellen sighed in a martyred tone.

"You certainly will," Ross promised her, and Ellen was much reassured by the look of desire he gave her when he made that promise.

CHAPTER ELEVEN

Ellen never had a doubt that she was doing the right thing in marrying Ross right up until the time she stood beside him at the altar. Then, however, one glimpse of his set, solemn face started a nagging little worry that she might have been too precipitate in feeling so complacently sure of herself.

Of course, the mere act of exchanging marital vows again might be the reason for his gravity. He had failed at marriage once, and he wouldn't have been human if he didn't feel just a little apprehensive that he might do so again. But he looked more than apprehensive. He looked as though he were attending a funeral instead of his own wedding!

Ellen tried to concentrate on the ceremony, but her thoughts were flying off in a hundred different directions. She was feeling a little sad herself at going through this ceremony again with someone other than John, but the sadness was tempered by her love for Ross and her realization that John himself would have been delighted that his best friend and his former wife, the two people he had cared more about than anyone in the world, were going to try to find happiness together now that he was gone.

Her thought that Ross looked as though he were attending a funeral made her try to recall how he had looked and acted at John's funeral, but it was all a blur. She couldn't even remember Ross being there, though she knew he had been. Then she felt a dart of fear as she realized she was making herself vulnerable once again to the sort of pain she had felt at losing John, should anything ever happen to Ross. And finally, she was just plain scared that Ross really didn't want to marry her, that he had been forced into making a decision he wasn't ready for through sheer jealousy and the inherent need certain men felt to protect and hold on to something they wanted when they thought someone else was going to try to take it away from them.

All in all, her second wedding wasn't anything like her first, nor was it anything like she had envisioned in the preceding three days of exultant joy when she had been so certain she and Ross were right for each other. She had even had the somewhat traitorous thought that they might be more right for each other than she and John had been, since their interests and outlook were certainly more alike than had been the case with her and John.

She somehow managed to say her vows with steady calmness, but when it came time for Ross to kiss her at the end of the ceremony, her eyes must have betrayed some of what she was feeling, for Ross first frowned slightly, then gave her a reassuring smile. And his kiss was as gently tender and loving as she could have wished for, reassuring her to a certain degree that she was simply suffering from wedding jitters.

Then they were immersed in the clamoring, joyous good wishes of their friends and being rushed off to a local restaurant for a wedding luncheon and there was no more time to worry about whether she had done the right thing. Indeed, her mood lightened considerably once it was patently too late to back out anyway, and her smiles and laughter were genuine as she responded to the well-meaning teasing of her friends. Too, Ross's earlier gravity fell away after the ceremony, and he was attentive, loving, and lighthearted enough himself to make her doubt he had ever looked so gloomy.

Rosie was smugly self-congratulatory at having her instincts confirmed, and exuberantly confident that Ross and Ellen were made for each other. And as Ross and Ellen were preparing to leave for the ranch, a honeymoon being impossible for the present, Rosie whispered gleefully to Ellen, "I knew you and Ross would get together once you got over hating each other's guts. You were never meant to be a politician's wife, honey. You'd rather pitch hay for horses and cows than pitch political slogans to a crowd."

Ellen stared at her in dismay as for the first time in three days she remembered she had a date with Joel Blake Sunday evening, and she hadn't so much as given the man a thought!

"What's the matter?" Rosie asked in alarm. "Did I say something wrong?"

"No, no, Rosie," Ellen whispered, looking anxiously at where Ross was taking his leave of Jake and the other men. "I just remembered I have a date with Joel on Sunday!" She practically wailed her dilemma, and Rosie stared at her in astonishment for an instant, then dissolved into chuckles.

"Don't you think you'd better cancel it?" she asked with a giggle, casting her eyes toward Ross. "I somehow don't think Ross is the type to share . . . at least not his wife!"

"Yes, of course," Ellen murmured distractedly. "I will. I just can't believe I forgot all about it until now!"

"Well, you have had a few other things on your mind," Rosie responded dryly, amusement making her brown eyes twinkle. "Do you want me to call Joel? I have the feeling you're going to be pretty busy for a while." She looked at Ross again, her smile wickedly anticipatory.

"No, I'll do it," Ellen said with a gloomy lack of anticipation on her part. "God, he'll never understand!"

"So what?" Rosie said practically. "He's part of your past now. It's your future with Ross that's important."

Ellen relaxed somewhat, and her smile was slightly dreamy as she agreed. "Yes. You're right as usual, Rosie. It will all work out."

She jumped as Ross's voice answered, and she realized he had heard only the last of her words and had misunderstood them. "It had better," he said with dry teasing, though his eyes weren't teasing at all when she looked up at him, "because I'll be damned if anyone is ever going to get me up in front of a preacher again. In this case, it's *two* strikes and I'm out."

Rosie laughed affectionately and gave him a big hug. "No need to worry, my friend," she asserted confidently. "I've never seen two people who had more in common than you and Ellen, and yet you've both got just enough spirit and temper to keep your marriage from getting boring. It should be interesting around the ranch for the next fifty years," she teased, tongue-in-cheek.

Ross looked directly into Ellen's eyes as he replied, though it was a look she found hard to decipher, except that he looked almost grimly determined. "Make that seventy-five years, Rosie. I plan to stick around a long time."

"Good for you," Rosie praised him loyally.

Ross grabbed her hand then and pulled her through the laughing throng of friends to the Corvette, his concession to the specialness of the occasion, since Ellen had objected to departing in his pickup. Minutes later they were alone and on their way to Ross's ranch—Ellen's new home—and her only regret was that the stickshift prevented her from cuddling up against him. She felt no need to talk, but was content to relish her newfound sense of belonging and

134

to gaze with prideful love at the delicately engraved golden wedding band on the third finger of her left hand. It came as a surprise to her then when Ross addressed her in a solemn voice to match the face he had worn at their wedding.

"I'm sorry we can't have a honeymoon yet, Ellen. Do you mind very much?"

She looked at him, surprised. "No, I don't mind, darling. Of course, I'd like to have you all to myself on some idyllic isle for a while, but I can wait until it's possible to go. Besides," she added complacently, "I love the ranch. I've always wanted to live on one," she confided happily.

"It's a lot of work," Ross replied in a carefully neutral voice. "You don't think you'll get tired of helping out? I am going to need your help, you know."

Far from minding, Ellen felt a prideful sense of sharing, and she told him so. "I'm not in the least afraid of hard work, Ross. I'd be hurt if you didn't let me help. I've always preferred outdoor work to housework anyway."

He cast a sceptical eye at her. "Does that mean you don't intend to do any housework?" he asked with dry teasing. "I can't afford to hire you a maid, and it might get a little gruesome if you spend all your time outdoors."

"Oh, I'll give the house a lick and a promise occasionally," she promised him with grave teasing. "But don't expect perfection. I'm not a fanatic about it."

To her surprise and relief, he murmured, "Good. A man likes to know he can put his feet on the coffee table without provoking a major fight."

Ellen put her hand on the back of his neck and ran her fingers through the thick hair she loved so. "You can put your feet anywhere you like, Mr. Sayer," she promised in a seductively low voice. "In fact, if I remember correctly, you once promised if I'd share your bed, you'd warm mine for me. I plan to hold you to that."

Ross cast her a lazy smile of male anticipation and laughed softly. "I plan to warm a lot more than your feet," he promised in a low, seductive voice. "And feel free to hold on to any part of me you please."

"Thank you. I will," Ellen murmured with loving teasing, then stretched across to give him a warm kiss on his cheek. He raised a hand from the steering wheel to caress her cheek and keep her face close to him for a moment, and his touch was so warm and arousing and comforting at the same time, that Ellen closed her eyes to savor it, feeling happier than at any time she could remember. "I love you, Ross," she whispered spontaneously. "And I'll do everything I can to make you happy."

"I know you will, honey," Ross answered in deep tones. "We're going to make it work."

There was such confidence in his voice that Ellen relaxed entirely then, sharing his confidence, feeling sweetly blissful and complete for the first time in a long while. When they reached the ranch, neither was in a mood to break the spell of the closeness they had attained and both were eager to affirm their marriage in ways other than with spoken vows.

Ross carried her over the threshold while she giggled and cautioned him that she didn't want to start married life by crippling her husband, whereupon he assured her solemnly that she didn't weigh much more than a steer he had wrestled once in a rodeo. Her resulting glare was only halfserious and changed to slumberous anticipation when he set her on her feet and gave her her first kiss in her new home from her new husband.

"Did you have time to buy any of that fancy underwear new brides always stock up on to entice their husbands before they start taking them for granted and wearing things like fuzzy pink coveralls?" he murmured teasingly,

136

his blue eyes caressing her deliciously as he ran his hands over her with the possessiveness of a new husband.

Ellen affected chagrined unhappiness. "Oh, Ross, I'm sorry," she apologized gravely. "I've been so busy that I'm afraid all I brought with me was a torn slip, a bra with sagging elastic, raggedy panties, and the pink fuzzies." She sighed regretfully. "I'm afraid I even forgot the black nightgown."

Ross regarded her sternly. "That's what I figured," he said with mock disgust. "It looks like I'm going to have to do everything myself in this marriage." He turned her toward the bedroom and gave her a little shove. "Come with me, woman," he ordered high-handedly. "You're about to find out you're married to a man who thinks of everything."

Ellen blinked at him in puzzlement over her shoulder, then hid a smile when she saw his stern expression ameliorated by a twinkle in his beautiful blue eyes. She marched in front of him to the bedroom, gave a little squeal of delight when she saw several elaborately wrapped packages in the center of the bed, then dived for them with uninhibited greed.

Her oohs and aahs and murmurs of delight were everything Ross could have wished for as she tore off the wrappings and pulled out complete sets of delicate, seductive lingerie right down to figure-hugging, see-through teddies and long, slinky nightgowns that would have embarrassed a mannequin in a store window.

"Oh, Ross," Ellen cooed at him in awed, pleasure-laden tones. "You're not only a man who thinks of everything, but you think in such exotic terms!"

He laughed, his smile under his mustache broad and confident. "Well, you have to view it from my perspective," he said tongue-in-cheek. "When you're working beside me in the barn shoveling manure, wearing dirty jeans

137

and your oldest shirt, I'm going to be concentrating on what's *under* the outer layer. It should make for some interesting workdays."

Ellen blinked up at him innocently. "How true," she said mildly. "I'm just sorry my own tastes lie in bare chests and other . . . er . . . natural attributes unadorned by exotic underclothing. Otherwise I'd have bought you some frillies too."

Ross froze for an instant at the word *frillies,* then his eyes warmed to a seductive glow. "Interested in the basics, are you?" he inquired curiously. And at her solemn nod he nodded himself with satisfaction. "Well, that's good, because you'd have a hell of a time getting me into any 'frillies,' as you call them."

Ellen cocked her head and studied him thoroughly, her heart rate picking up as she viewed his relaxed, masculine stance, the rugged physique under his suit, and the beloved handsomeness of his face. "That's what I thought," she said meekly, though the boldness of her stare belied that meekness. "Now, would you like me to put on some of this finery?" She gestured at the strewn silkenness surrounding her. "Underneath my dirty jeans and old shirt, of course," she added with innocent mockery.

"Forget the outer layer for the time being," Ross instructed her in a voice grown husky with desire. "There'll be plenty of time to dress for the world tomorrow. I want you to dress for me right now." He turned around and placed his hand on the doorknob, looking back at her with possessive anticipation as he said, "I'll go get the champagne I've been chilling. I don't think we're going to need much of it, as I'm already feeling pretty high, but it's traditional, isn't it?"

"Yes, darling. It's traditional," Ellen said softly, her gaze promising him that she was going to make him feel even higher without benefit of champagne. He acknowledged that look with a grin before he left the room.

She scrambled to clear the bed and debated for an agonized moment over which of the things he'd bought he'd most like to see her in, then grabbed up a filmy pale turquoise negligee that she knew instinctively would bring an answering color to her eyes, and dashed with it to the adjoining bathroom so that Ross wouldn't catch her in the middle of her dressing . . . or undressing as the case might be.

A few minutes later her eyes widened with something close to embarrassment as she viewed herself clad in the diaphanous material that actually hid nothing of importance while revealing all that was in enticing detail. Then she shrugged, grinned at herself, brushed her long mass of hair into a halo around her face and shoulders, took a deep breath, and stepped out into the bedroom again.

Ross had discarded his coat and tie and was lying on the bed in a relaxed position with his white shirt unbuttoned down to his impressive chest, his trouser-clad legs crossed one over the other. He was propped up on a couple of pillows with a full glass of champagne in his hand and another full one on the bedside table beside him.

His blue eyes lit with masculine appreciation as Ellen crossed slowly to his side, then they warmed with unabashed arousal as he watched the folds of the gown reveal and conceal alternately in enticing waves around her.

"If I do say so myself, I have excellent taste," Ross murmured appreciatively, "both in nightgowns and in women."

Ellen might have disputed that assertion if she had cared to recall Tina to mind at that moment, but she didn't, and instead she gave herself over to sheer pleasure that Ross found her beautiful. "Of course, you do," she

139

agreed in low, sexy, teasing tones. "You married *me*, didn't you?"

"Umm-hmm," Ross agreed, swinging his legs over the side of the bed to sit up. "And I think a husband has certain conjugal rights I'm beginning to be most anxious to take advantage of." He got to his feet, reached down to pick up Ellen's glass of champagne, and handed it to her. "Shall we drink a toast to us, Ellen?" he asked, his eyes devouring her, the desire in them made twice as exciting by the deeper glint of love she saw there.

"Yes, to us, Ross," Ellen said softly, raising the glass to her lips to take a large swallow in keeping with the heart-felt sincerity she wanted the toast to hold.

She was pleased when Ross downed the entire contents of the glass in one swallow, then set the glass aside. She hastily finished hers, superstitiously not wanting to leave any of the liquid in the glass in case it might negate the toast. Then Ross took her face into his large, powerful hands and gazed into her eyes, his own glowing with sincerity. "I'm glad you're my wife, Ellen," he said softly. "I want to make you happy."

"You will, Ross," Ellen said shakily, gulping down the lump in her throat that came as a result of his words and his look. "You will."

He smiled a lazy, pleasing smile. "I know one way already that I can make you happy," he whispered seductively. "Want me to show you?"

Ellen nodded, her eyes big with anticipation, her lovely mouth trembling slightly with the emotions that filled her to overflowing. "Sometimes I'm thick-headed," she cautioned Ross solemnly. "You have to show me things over and over again."

His smile broadened. "I'm a patient man," he assured her. "I'll be glad to show you as often as you like." And then Ellen watched fascinated as his mustached lips came closer and closer until they closed over hers in an enveloping, warmly wet possession she met with melting eagerness and love. Those wonderful lips of his were all hers now, she found herself thinking lightheadedly as Ross deepened the kiss, thrusting his tongue into her mouth with a growing impatience to taste all of her. She felt the powerful length of his body and knew that it was all hers now, too, reveling in the knowledge and in the delicious feel of his muscles rippling under her hands as he pulled her closer into his body.

"Come to bed, wife," he growled against her mouth as he pulled her backward with him to fall across the bed. "I want you. I want to be inside you again and know you belong to me!"

Ellen wanted the same thing every bit as passionately as Ross did, and her hands were shaking as she helped him rid himself of his clothing until he was bared to her exploration. The beautiful gown was disposed of next, and then, incredibly, it was as though it was the first time the two of them had made love. Each stroked the other with almost reverent exploration, their eyes reflecting wonder that what they held was now theirs alone. But, inevitably, the tentative, warm caresses grew bolder, the stroking more erotic, until their breathing had quickened to unbearable tension, and their locked gazes were drugged with the wanting and need each felt.

Ellen spoke first, on a gasp, as Ross's knowing fingers found a place that sparked her already overflowing senses into flame. "Ross . . . please! Make me your wife in every way!"

Ross's voice was deeply toned with husky satisfaction as he moved over her and felt her legs parting to receive him with sweetly eager urgency. "My beautiful, greedy, impatient wife!" he husked with no trace of condemnation of such qualities in his new bride. "Do you want your husband?" he asked with grating urgency. "Do you want all of me?"

"All of you!" Ellen urged, arching to meet him with impatient need, closing her eyes against the drugging blaze of passion in his that ignited her senses unbearably.

"Then look at me while I take you, sweet Ellen," he instructed in a voice both harsh and gentle. "I want to see what happens in those big eyes of yours when I give you all you want and more!"

Ellen's eyes came open even as she felt Ross's thrust, darkened and half-closed again as she moaned her response to the feel of his dominant, throbbing manhood filling her to the brim of completion, then widened in hypnotic bondage to the fiercely possessive command in his own. And all the while his body led hers in the timeless rhythm of love, his eyes held her soul and heart in ever more tightening, binding ownership until she cried out her submission to his possession in all ways in an aching, shuddering expression of ecstasy that triggered Ross's submission to his own needs in a convulsive explosion that rocked the both of them to their cores.

It was a long, long time before Ross finally raised himself to his elbows, stroked the damp moistness of tousled hair away from Ellen's forehead, and smiled down at her with a serenity she had never seen in him before.

"We're man and wife now, Ellen," he said gently. "We may even have started a family in the process of sealing that fact." He took a deep breath, and his eyes were rock steady as he added, "And God help anybody who ever tries to take either away from me."

"Amen to that," Ellen said softly, her love shining at him from the large, luminiscent eyes he had watched so carefully as he had made her his own.

CHAPTER TWELVE

It was Saturday before Ellen found an opportunity to call
Joel Blake and cancel their date. Ross had kept her beside
him almost constantly, showing her around the ranch,
beginning to educate her in ways she could help, or, quite
simply, making love to her. She was enraptured by the
time she spent with him, but had nevertheless grown quite
nervous by the time he was called away by one of his hands
on Saturday morning, leaving her sleepy and tired from a
most satisfactory night with him, and wondering where on
earth he found the energy to bound off to work like that
when he had certainly not spent the greater part of the
night sleeping!

Part of her longed to confide in Ross and tell him she
had to call Joel and inform him of her marriage, but
another part, the cautious part, told her Ross's reaction
might skirt the edges of disaster. In the end it was beyond
her to take the chance of upsetting the delicate balance of
trust and belonging they were beginning to share, and so
she dragged herself out of bed after he had left that morning and went straight to the telephone to get the matter
off her mind and into the past where it belonged.

It took a while to locate Joel, and, in fact, she had to
leave her number and await his return call, a development
that increased her nervousness as she had no idea how
long Ross would be away. She was a great deal relieved

when the call came before Ross did, but her nervousness was apparent in her voice when she spoke to Joel.

"Hi, sweetheart!" he came on the line after one of his aides had placed the call for him. "I was going to call you today to tell you where to meet me tomorrow night. Did you think I'd forgotten?" he asked cheerfully.

Ellen winced at his remark about forgetting, since that was exactly what she had done herself for far too long. "Ah . . . no, Joel," she faltered, desperately searching for some tactful way to tell him what she had to. "You see, the thing is—" she started, only to have him break in.

"I can't tell you how much I'm looking forward to tomorrow night, Ellen," Joel said with intimate anticipation. "Things have gotten so hectic with the campaign heating up, if I didn't have this breather with you coming up, I think I'd be tempted to chuck the whole thing!"

Oh, God! Ellen thought with gloomy desperation. *That's just what I needed to hear right now!* "Joel!" she forced herself to break into his continuing eulogy to what he expected for the following evening. "The thing is I can't come tomorrow night after all!" she got out in a rush, knowing she shouldn't say it so bluntly, but pushed to the point of recklessness.

There was a dead silence for a moment, then Joel's disappointment came clearly over the line. "Why not, Ellen?" he asked quietly. "Whatever the conflict is, can't you put it off for a while? I really need to see you, honey."

"It's not that simple, Joel," Ellen replied somewhat grimly, her nerves tautening as she found her task so much more difficult than she had anticipated, and she had never thought it would be easy! Then she took a deep breath and stated the facts baldly. "Joel, I got married on Wednesday."

This time the dead silence lasted longer than a minute.

Finally, Joel said, increduously, "You're kidding!" And then, more calmly, "Why?"

"Why?" Ellen repeated, feeling the reason should have been evident. "Joel, I told you I was emotionally involved with someone. I know I did."

"Yes, but you also said it wasn't working out!" Joel said heatedly.

"Well, at the time, it wasn't!" Ellen said, becoming irritated, but struggling to control it. "Then . . . well, it did . . . obviously!"

"Damn it, Ellen!" Joel's frustration and anger were obvious, though why he should have built so much upon one date, Ellen didn't know. She had to remind herself forcibly that there was absolutely no reason for Joel to react so strongly when the two of them had barely begun a relationship! "Who is he?" Joel now asked, his tone almost belligerent.

Ellen sighed. "Ross Sayer," she supplied, seeing no reason to withhold the information. "He was a dear friend of my late husband's," she added, perhaps hoping to convince Joel that she hadn't married a total stranger, though her patience with Joel's unrealistic possessiveness was fast running out.

"Do you love him?" Joel continued his questioning, still in a harsh tone.

"Well, of course!" Ellen gritted, trying to maintain her temper. "Why else would I marry him?"

She didn't hear Joel's next question because a slight sound behind her alerted her to the fact that she was no longer alone. She swung around to face wide-eyed the stony, dangerously unyielding countenance of her husband staring at her from across the room. Ross looked positively furious in a tightly held, threatening way, and Ellen's heart gave an alarming thump at that expression. Her eyes slid away from his guiltily even as she knew it was the wrong thing to do, but it was impossible to meet that flint-hard gaze with any degree of equanimity.

"Joel, I've got to go!" she cut in on whatever Joel had been saying, impatient to the point of desperation to cut the conversation short and begin to erase the expression on Ross's face that was breaking her heart. "I'm sorry," she interrupted Joel again as it became apparent he was in no hurry to oblige her by hanging up. "Good-bye, Joel!" she said forcefully as she took matters into her own hands and hung up on him. Then she jumped as she felt Ross's hand descend upon her shoulder without any noticeable gentleness. As he gripped her shoulder and began to turn her toward him, she turned in a rush herself and threw her arms around his waist, burying her head on his chest.

"I love you!" she cried out, squeezing him so hard she heard him grunt, and not only with surprise. She raised her head then and began to babble almost incoherently. "Yes, that was Joel Blake, but it didn't mean anything, Ross! We had a date, you see, only I can't go now, and naturally, he was a little put out because I didn't invite him to the wedding." She stopped, winced, then corrected herself. "I mean I didn't *tell* him about the wedding. I forgot about it, see?"

Ross was regarding her with a strange look, though Ellen was wholeheartedly relieved to see that he didn't seem angry any longer, but merely puzzled and about as exasperated as a man could be without crossing back over the line into anger again. "You forgot the wedding?" he asked with dry sarcasm.

"What?" Ellen asked, puzzled in her turn for an instant, until she realized what he meant. Then she frowned. "No, no!" she said forcefully. "I forgot about the *date!*"

"What date?" Ross asked with smooth dangerousness.

"The date I had with Joel for tomorrow night!" Ellen

explained eagerly, then faltered as she saw that dangerous look again. "I made it before you proposed," she said very carefully, "and then I forgot about it. I haven't had a chance to break it until now, and I didn't want you to get upset, so I waited until you were gone to call Joel."

"And what makes you think I would have been upset?" Ross asked with innocent inquiry that dripped sarcasm at the end.

"Well, you are, aren't you?" Ellen asked cautiously. "Upset, I mean."

Ross looked as though he wanted to throttle her for a moment, then he drawled, "It does tend to upset me when my wife makes dates with another man, yes. I'm funny that way."

Ellen shook her head frustratedly. "But I made it *before* you proposed, Ross! And then I forgot all about it! Doesn't that tell you anything about how unimportant it was to me?"

Ross didn't reply directly and his eyes narrowed as he asked, "What did you mean when you said to Blake, 'Why else would I marry him?' "

Ellen looked surprised. "He asked me if I loved you, and I said I did. And then I said, 'Why else would I marry him?' "

Ross studied her intently for several seconds, then his features relaxed as he evidently saw the sincerity in Ellen's face. "Is that the end of Joel Blake then?" he asked on a hard note.

Ellen nodded emphatically. "Yes, of course. I'm your wife, Ross. I love you. I'm not going to be seeing Joel Blake anymore except maybe on television." She smiled hesitantly then and reached up to cup Ross's cheek. "But if you don't mind, I still plan to vote for him."

Ross regarded her silently, then shrugged. "The voting

booth is sacrosanct, I suppose, but I don't know if *I'll* vote for him now."

"Ross," Ellen teased him gently. "You don't really want four more years of old wishy-washy Cunningham, do you?"

He didn't reply, merely continued to stare down into her softly loving eyes with the momentary pain in his own slowly fading away. "I guess we've just had our first married fight?" he asked thoughtfully.

Ellen sighed and nodded. "Yes, and I'm afraid it may not be our last. You have a rotten temper, Ross," she said self-righteously as though she herself were possessed of the temperament of a saint.

"*I* have a rotten temper?!" Ross replied on an incredulous snort. "And you're a sweetheart, I suppose?"

Ellen blinked at him sweetly. "I'm too modest to say," she replied demurely.

Ross muttered a quiet expletive by way of an answer that made Ellen look at him with offended dignity. Then he wrapped a hand in the mass of her hair and tilted her head up to look at him. "Well, *sweetheart,*" he drawled dryly, "if this is our first fight, I believe there's a time-honored way of making up, isn't there?"

Ellen tried to look reticently naive and failed miserably when a grin took command of her lips. "After last night?" she asked, managing to sound tiredly incredulous.

"What's the matter, can't you take it like a man?" Ross mocked her mercilessly. "Puny, are you? A weakling? Not up to snuff?"

Ellen glared at him, circled his neck with both arms, and planted a fierce kiss on him that missed his mouth and left her with a mouthful of mustache. She drew back and scowled at him. "I'll show you who can take it and who can't!" she threatened direly. "Before I'm through with you, you're the one who'll be crying uncle!"

"Want to bet?" Ross asked with a leering smile, bending down to scoop her up into his arms. "We'll see, Miss Toughie," he promised as he headed for the bedroom. "One of us will cry uncle all right, but the other of us is merciless!"

"Hardhearted Hannah is my middle name," Ellen responded stubbornly, then yelped as Ross pinched her breast with just enough pressure to sting. "Brute abuse will get you nowhere, buster!" she threatened, though even the slight sting hadn't prevented a sharp flash of desire from racing through her veins.

"Maybe not," Ross agreed judiciously as he tossed her onto the bed and started to remove his shirt. "But I'm certain superior strength will," he added with cocky self-confidence. "This is still a man's world, baby," he growled with mock fierceness. "Especially out on the ranch."

"We're in the bedroom, not out in the pasture though," Ellen reminded him sweetly, rising to her knees to shrug out of her robe and then her sheer white nightgown. She faced him with hands on her hips, thrusting out her breasts provocatively. "Choose your weapons, sir," she challenged him with a stern look.

Ross stepped out of his jeans, eyeing her with a practiced and appreciative eye. "No, you choose yours, honey," he invited softly as he tossed the jeans aside and came to tower over her. "You're not the only one with something to offer."

At that, Ellen threw back her head and laughed uninhibitedly, then stretched out loving arms to welcome her husband to bed. "Come on then, darling," she invited coaxingly. "I'm anxious to see who wins this battle."

"Ha!" Ross laughed back as he came to her. "You aren't even going to place, though you certainly know how to show!"

And sometime later, though Ellen cried mercy purely as a matter of policy, it was tacitly understood that the battle was a gloriously fought tie, leaving both participants unqualified winners!

CHAPTER THIRTEEN

For the next three months Ellen led what she privately considered a charmed life. She took to ranch life like a duck to water, reveling in the long hours out of doors in the glorious countryside, loving the red and white cows with their beautiful brown eyes and the horses that were such a joy to ride, making friends with the cowhands who worked for Ross, acquiring a mongrel dog someone let out by the roadside and that she insisted on taking home.

She waited with eager patience for any signs that she might have become pregnant, but was not unduly distressed when she didn't find them. She was having much too good a time to let much of anything worry her, and she had faith that a baby would come in its own time.

Ross was proving to be a dream of a husband, much easier and more tolerant than she would ever have expected, patient to a fault at helping her learn what she needed and wanted to know, possessed of a sense of roguish humor that never failed to delight her, and increasingly pleasing to her both in bed and out of it, though she would have sworn he couldn't have gotten any better!

Perhaps it was inevitable that such an idyllic existence couldn't remain unmarred, but their next fight nevertheless took her by surprise, and she reacted twice as volubly due to the unexpectedness of the conflict.

There had been a violent autumn storm one evening,

151

and the next morning Ellen and Ross went out looking for any damage, finding it to be much worse than they had expected, since lightning had struck the old barn where Ross stored hay for the horses and cattle to eat during the winter months. Ross eyed the damage with a grim look that made Ellen hurt for him.

"We can get it fixed before winter, can't we?" she asked encouragingly, wanting to comfort him.

"We could if I had the money," he responded harshly, kicking at a burned bale of hay. "Since I don't, I'll have to sell off some cattle to pay for it."

Ellen looked at him with startled surprise. They hadn't discussed finances so far, and she had no idea what resources Ross possessed other than the obvious ones of the ranch and the livestock. "What?" she asked blankly, certain she must have misunderstood.

Ross gave her an impatient look. "I said I don't have the cash to rebuild right now. The best I can manage are some half-assed repairs to get us through the winter." He eyed the barn grimly again. "I've needed to pull this down for a long time, but the money was never there."

Ellen thought a moment, realizing the money she had would build a fine new barn without substantially denting the capital. The trick lay in convincing Ross it was her right to help out financially, just as she was doing physically. Nothing subtle came to her, however, so she ended by blurting out the proposition. "I can help, Ross," she said with cautious eagerness. "I have plenty of money, and we could have a great new barn built in no time at . . . all." She faltered on the last two words as Ross swung around to look at her with angry blue eyes, his mouth formed into a stubborn line.

"No," he denied her offer harshly. "That was one of the conditions, remember? I'm not using a penny of your money on this place!"

His reaction sparked Ellen's own temper, though she should have realized Ross was reacting more from disappointed frustration than from actual hostility toward her. "And why not?" she asked spiritedly. "It seems to me that . . ."

"Forget it, Ellen!" he said harshly, turning his back on her to look once again at the damage. "I said no, and I meant no!" He started to stride away back toward the house then, and after staring at his rigid back for a moment of angry frustration, Ellen ran to catch up to him.

"Now just a damned minute, Ross Sayer!" she blurted at him as she caught at his arm to stop him. "I'm part of this family too!"

Ross stopped and looked down at her wearily. "Nobody said you weren't," he said gruffly. "But that doesn't mean you have to strip yourself financially to help out. A ranch can be a bottomless pit where money is concerned. There's always something that needs buying or doing, and I won't have you—"

"What do you mean, you won't have me?" Ellen demanded hot-temperedly, ignoring the immediate flare of anger in Ross's eyes at her tone. "Correct me if I'm wrong, but when we married, didn't this ranch become half mine?"

Ross stiffened, making Ellen even more angry. She knew how much Ross loved the ranch, and she interpreted his attitude as selfishness on his part, thinking he didn't want to share ownership of his beloved ranch with her. That hurt, not from any mercenary aspect, but rather from a sense of being excluded from some part of his life. All of a sudden she felt as though she didn't belong anymore, that she was a tenant instead of a full-fledged partner, and perhaps a temporary tenant at that!

Her hurt banished her common sense entirely, and she forgot that the one sure way to destroy any desire Ross

153

might have for compromise was to challenge him directly. He was very male in that respect, and if she had been herself, she would have softened her tone and her attitude and approached him reasonably instead of flying off at the handle.

"Well, this ranch *is* half mine," she sputtered angrily at him, "and if it needs a new barn, it's damned well going to get a new barn!" She turned sharply away from him, not wanting to show that she was close to tears of hurt and angry frustration and bruised feelings. She had taken no more than two steps before Ross caught hold of her arm and jerked her around, his face set and closed and utterly indomitable.

"Listen to me, Ellen," he said with quiet dangerousness. "I don't give a damn what your *legal* rights are," and he sneered the one word contemptuously. "This is *my* ranch . . . *my* responsibility. You make one move to send anyone out here to build a new barn with your money, and I'll kick their tails off this land so fast, their heads will spin! Do you understand me?"

Ellen's face whitened at the harshness of his grip on her and because she interpreted his words as confirmation that she was little better than hired help in his estimation. Indeed, she wondered if she herself might be one of those people he wouldn't hesitate to kick off *his* land.

"Yes, I understand," she barely whispered, her eyes going remote, some part of her retreating from Ross, some part of her dying a little in that retreat. She was an all-or-nothing person, and, to her mind, Ross had just told her she could never be all to him.

He seemed puzzled at her sudden lack of spirit, then became aware of how hard he was gripping her and loosened his hold with a grimace of distaste, though that was his only expression of apology. He was still too wrought up to soften measurably.

Ellen pulled herself out of his slackened hold and stepped back a pace. "I have some housework to do," she said without expression, turning on her heel to make her way back to the house. She thought she heard him call her name in a soft, exasperated tone, but she elected not to hear and continued on her way, her back straight, her head up, her eyes barely conscious of her surroundings, while she made her way to the house more by instinct than by purpose.

Once there, as was her habit, she began to work furiously at cleaning the house, using her muscles to deaden the protest in her mind. She refused to think about what had happened just then. She knew there would come a time when she would have to come to terms with this new revelation of the character of the man she'd married, but she was incapable of doing so for the present. The shock was too great. The ramifications were too frightening.

She worked like that all day, forgetting to eat, not even wondering why Ross didn't come to the house for lunch. She was an automaton, shelving her thoughts and her feelings in favor of mindless, soothing manual labor until suddenly it was dinnertime and there was nothing left to do anyway but cook.

She prepared the evening meal, placed it on the table, looked at it, found it revolting, and left it where it was untouched. Instead, she headed for the shower where she stood under the warm waves of water for a long time, letting them soothe her aching muscles and her troubled emotions as well. When she came out, she hesitated about dressing again, deciding instead to wear one of the gowns she had bought herself before her marriage to Ross, contrary to what she'd told him on their wedding day, refusing to realize that her reluctance to wear one he'd bought her was another form of withdrawal from him. Then she

155

climbed into bed, turned off the bedside light, and fell immediately into a deep sleep.

Sometime later she roused enough to feel him climbing into bed beside her. She had her back to him, and she didn't turn over, willing herself to go back to sleep. Ross spoke softly to her in the dark.

"We got most of the debris cleaned up at the barn. It doesn't look too bad." And when she didn't reply, he said, "I'm sorry I was late for dinner. I lost track of time. It didn't look as though you had any. Weren't you hungry?"

She forced herself to mumble something incoherent, wanting him to be quiet and let her go back to the peaceful oblivion of sleep. He hesitated for a few moments, then placed his warm hand on her shoulder. She didn't react in any way whatsoever, not even to flinch away from him. She lay as still and quiet as though she'd gone back to sleep.

Ross whispered, "Ellen?" And when she didn't answer, he moved closer. "Ellen?" he said again, kissing her on the shoulder where his hand lay.

Still she didn't react, and after a while he moved away to his own side of the bed, and a little later she heard the deep breathing that signaled he was asleep. But sleep had fled from her, and she lay for long hours staring up at the shadowed ceiling, thinking hard about the fact that this was the first night of their marriage they hadn't made love, wondering sadly why she didn't feel any desire to make love with her husband, not on that night, and not for many nights to come.

The next morning Ross was subdued with her, eyeing her speculatively across the breakfast table from time to time. She went about her business without making conversation, not avoiding eye contact with him, but not seeking it either. Finally, he remarked conversationally, "We could have used your help yesterday. I saw that you wer-

156

en't kidding about doing housework. The house practically glows," he added half-humorously. "But could you help us out today, Ellen?" he added more quietly. "You're needed."

She raised calm eyes to his, eyes that didn't sparkle and glow as they used to, and said equally quietly. "Of course, Ross. Just tell me what you'd like me to do."

He frowned slightly, not liking her lack of animation at all, liking even less the nebulous tone in her voice he didn't understand. He didn't realize she was not responding as a wife now, but rather like someone he was hiring to do a job. "Okay," he said with slow thoughtfulness. "Will you join us at the barn when you're through in here?"

Ellen nodded and began gathering dishes to take to the dishwasher while Ross stared at her for a long moment, then got to his feet and left the house. When Ellen joined the men later, she threw herself into any job that came to hand, working with an almost demonic energy that had Ross frowning in her direction more than once, looking as though he wanted to ask her to slow down. He didn't, however, and by the end of the day Ellen was so exhausted that after no more than nibbling at her supper, she went to bed and sleep again, this time not even half-waking when Ross joined her.

That became the pattern of their days for the next week or so, Ross beginning to look grimmer and grimmer as the barrier between him and Ellen rose higher and higher, and Ellen looking slimmer and slimmer since food held no appeal for her and she was expending enormous amounts of energy.

Finally, Ross informed her he had invited Rosie and Jake to Sunday dinner, and Ellen nodded, which was becoming more her habit these days than speech. Ross's jaw tightened and he got up and flung himself out of the house on some imaginary errand rather than express his growing frustration and anger.

Rosie was obviously shocked when she saw Ellen that Sunday, but she wisely kept her distress to herself, electing to maintain a cheerful atmosphere that she was gratified to see was beginning to relax Ellen into speaking in other than monosyllables after an hour or so. At the dinner table, however, Jake unfortunately brought up the subject of the barn.

"You ought to rebuild that old heap from the ground up, Ross," Jake informed his host bluntly. "I'm surprised it took lightning to hurt it. A strong wind could have knocked it over at any time during the last two years."

Aside from a slight stiffening, Ross took Jake's comments in good part. "I know, Jake," he said wryly. "I will rebuild it one of these days."

Rosie noticed the almost bitter look Ellen shot Ross, however, the first time actually that Ellen had let her feelings break through since the day when Ross had rejected her offer—no, her demand!—to help. Rosie's brown eyes widened with unhappy sympathy as it dawned on her that something was really wrong between Ross and Ellen, and she determined then and there to get to the source of it.

"Can't you convince Ross he's wasting his time trying to repair that junkheap, Ellen?" she asked deliberately, uncaring that she was being less than tactful.

Her heart sank when Ellen gave her an unamused smile. "Who, me?" she replied with wide-eyed innocence. "I'm just one of the troops, Rosie." She nodded her head coolly at Ross. "Ross is the general. He makes policy."

Rosie glanced at Ross and saw his eyes frost over and his jaw tighten into a stubborn line, and she gave an inner sigh of dismay as she discerned what the problem was. Ross's stubborn pride and Ellen's notorious generosity were in direct conflict and likely to remain so if they were left to their own devices.

"Hmmm," she murmured noncommittally. "Don't give Jake any ideas, Ellen. I've convinced him that marriage is a full partnership, and I like things the way they are. He's even going to be in the delivery room with me when Junior here"—and she patted her rounded stomach complacently—"finally decides to stop hitching a ride and carry his own weight."

"Ha!" Jake laughed, reaching to spear himself another slice of ham. "I'll probably faint, but I'm game, all right. I helped create the little beggar, and I'm damned if I'll let Rosie chauffeur him into the world all on her own."

The discussion turned to the baby then, though Rosie almost wished it hadn't when she saw Ellen eyeing her stomach with wistful longing. However, she was too busy making inner plans to dissolve the conflict between Ross and Ellen to linger long over regrets at having introduced another touchy subject.

Immediately after dinner, while Rosie and Ellen were clearing the dishes, Rosie bluntly went on the attack. "What's the matter between you and Ross, Ellen?" she asked in a firm, no-nonsense tone.

Ellen looked startled, then wary. "What makes you think anything is wrong?" she prevaricated.

"Come on, Ellen!" Rosie responded with brusque impatience. "You must have lost ten pounds, Ross looks like he was carved out of granite, and the atmosphere between you two is thick enough to cut with a knife!" She softened somewhat when she saw the unhappiness in Ellen's eyes. "Come on, honey," Rosie urged. "I know you can tell me it's none of my business, but maybe a new perspective will help. And you know how much I love both of you, don't you?"

Ellen hesitated, then perched herself on a kitchen stool,

159

forgetting about the dirty dishes. Her soft mouth trembled as she wondered if she should confide in Rosie, but when she looked up and saw the soft sympathy in Rosie's warm brown eyes, it was her undoing.

"Oh, Rosie," she sniffed, on the verge of tears. "He doesn't really love me. Oh, he wants me, all right," she added, sounding somewhat bitter, the words flowing out of her now that she had gotten over the first hurdle, "but he doesn't understand what real love is all about. He treats me like . . . like a hired hand!"

The tears spilled over then, though she was far from being hysterical. She didn't have the energy for hysteria. Rosie thought she looked like a little girl rather than a woman perched on the stool like that, shoulders hunched dejectedly and mouth puckered up, so Rosie went to her and wrapped a comforting arm over her shoulder. "Tell me about it," she invited warmly.

And Ellen did, the words spilling out, sometimes half-disjointedly, until at last she ended with, "And that's it, Rosie! That's the whole problem! Ross doesn't want to share with me, and he won't let me share with him!" And then, with bitter denunciation, she added, "I hate Tina! She just ruined him!"

Rosie looked a little askance at that and wisely refrained from comment. "Well, honey," she replied in her usual practical way, "it looks to me like you and Ross have more of a communication problem than anything else." And at Ellen's sceptical look, Rosie asked, "Have you told him how you really feel about this? How important it is to you?"

Ellen looked sulky. "No, and I'm not going to!" she said with defiant crossness. "You can't change someone's character just because it hurts you. It wouldn't do any good to talk to him. He's too damned stubborn!"

Rosie cocked an eyebrow as she mentally reflected that

Ross was not the only member of this particular marriage who had a stubborn streak! Instead of saying so, however, she merely commented mildly that she hoped everything would work out.

"Ha!" Ellen disputed that, jumping from the stool to begin slinging dishes into the dishwasher with dangerous energy. "Fat chance!"

Rosie excused herself then, saying she needed to go to the bathroom, but instead she headed straight for Ross and Jake, gave Jake an eye signal that politely told him to get lost, and when he was obliging enough to do so, Rosie pounced on Ross with a great deal less tact than she had used on Ellen.

"You thick-headed dunce!" she started out bluntly, ignoring the look Ross gave her that said he was less than appreciative of her description. "You haven't got a clue what Ellen's all about, do you?" she persisted, her tone disgusted. "You think every woman is just like Tina was— out for everything she can get!" Rosie seated herself across from Ross in a huffy movement that Ross eyed sardonically.

"Been having a little girl talk, have you?" he asked with dangerous quietness. But when Rosie stared right back at him without giving an inch, he sighed heavily and kept his patience. "No, I don't think every woman is like Tina, Rosie. I know you're not, and Ellen isn't either."

"You're darned right Ellen isn't!" Rosie pounced again. "She hasn't got a selfish bone in her body." She held up a hand when Ross would have spoken and rushed on. "In fact, she's so generous, it actually hurts her not to be able to help those she loves. Especially you! You're the one she loves most in the world!"

Ross looked stern and uncomfortable for an instant, then he firmed up again. "If you're talking about that cursed barn, Rosie, you can forget it. I've made up my mind on that subject!"

"And a closed mind is a dandy thing to have!" Rosie responded sarcastically, then went on, trying to sound more reasonable. "Ross, listen," she spoke very firmly. "That attitude may seem admirable to you, but to Ellen it's an indication that you don't love her. Are you aware she thinks you regard her as little better than hired, live-in help?"

Ross looked startled, then shocked, then grim, and shifted from a relaxed posture to tenseness. "That's stupid!" he growled. Then he looked slightly worried. "She's been working too hard lately though. I've thought about trying to stop her, but I've been so damned mad at her!" He broke off, obviously regretting his words, and his face closed up again.

"Yes, anyone can tell you're mad at her," Rosie agreed sardonically. "But what I don't understand is *why* you're mad at her. All she did was offer to help you, you idiot! And when you turned her down, she took it as evidence that you aren't really going to let her share in your life. She shares one hundred percent, Ross, and she can't understand anyone doing less."

"Does she?" Ross asked somewhat stiffly, his mind on the bedroom where the climate had been extremely arctic lately. His eyes involuntarily strayed toward that room, and Rosie, sharp as a tack, made the connection in an instant. She couldn't help the grin that stretched her mouth then, though she knew Ross was in no mood to appreciate humor at the moment.

"Cut you off, has she?" she asked innocently.

She wished she'd curbed her tongue when she saw the dark flush spread over Ross's rugged face and saw the dangerous glint of ice in his clear blue eyes. "Isn't that the one weapon women normally employ when they want to bring a man to heel?" he asked with cold sarcasm.

Rosie grew serious immediately. "That's another way you don't understand women, Ross," she said gently. "Our heads and our bodies are connected. When things aren't right emotionally, a lot of us can't separate our feelings from our bodies. It isn't done to punish our men. It's simply that we *can't* want sex when our hearts and our feelings are hurting."

Ross looked sceptical, but then he seemed to accept Rosie's explanation. "Men aren't so different," he commented grudgingly. "I haven't been exactly chomping at the bit either."

Rosie shrugged. "See?" she said practically. Then she got back to business. "The question is, what do you plan to do about this? Are you going to let your stubborn pride cause a rift between you and Ellen that might not be mendable? She considers everything she has is yours as well, Ross. It's that simple."

Ross ran an impatient, exasperated hand through his thick mane of hair. "It *isn't* that simple, Rosie. I want Ellen to maintain her financial security. I told her a ranch could eat money like it was going out of style, and I can envision her penniless if anything ever happened to me because she put it all into this place. I don't want that. I want to think of her as being taken care of."

Rosie's brown eyes glinted shrewdly as she studied Ross. "Are you sure you told her all of that in just that way, Ross?" she asked quietly.

He thought about it for a while, then shrugged. "Maybe not quite in that much detail," he admitted uncomfortably.

"Then I suggest you do," Rosie submitted dryly. "And furthermore, I suggest that a compromise is in order.

Surely you can take some of what she's offering—enough to make her feel like she's your true partner in this marriage—and still leave her enough to ensure her security?"

Ross gazed back at Rosie, his irritation fading finally into an affectionate smile. "Did you ever consider going into the marriage-counseling business, Rosie?" he asked dryly. "I think you've missed your calling."

She laughed. "No, I haven't," she assured him confidently. "I'm quite happy doing what I am with my life. It's just that sometimes an objective eye and ear and a nosy nature can be of help." Her mischievous smile made Ross laugh, and he got to his feet, pulled her up, and gave her an affectionate hug.

Rosie drew back laughing. "Don't damage my passenger," she teased him, rubbing her tummy. "And by the way," she added, "far be it from me to butt in to someone else's life," she said with false demureness, ignoring Ross's snort of disbelief, "but I noticed Ellen eyeing my tummy with a great deal of envy. Are the two of you considering having a baby?"

Ross fixed her with a stern look of disapproval. "Now, that's enough, Rosie!" he said firmly. "You take care of your own tummy and leave Ellen's to me."

Rosie shrugged unconcernedly at his putdown, her eyes sparkling wickedly. "Okay," she said innocently. "Just trying to help. And speaking of being a help, I think it's time Jake and I got out of the way and let you and Ellen do some serious talking for a change." She eyed Ross's sudden inner preoccupation with a great deal of satisfaction and turned away yelling, "Jake! Hey, Jake! Let's go home! Junior wants a nap!"

Jake came ambling into the room again, eyeing his wife and Ross with a great deal of curiosity, then was followed by Ellen, who began to protest their decision to leave.

"But you haven't been here long!" she protested, sending Rosie a pleading look. "I thought we'd play some cards or something."

"Not today," Rosie demurred blithely. "This pregnancy business upsets my whole schedule. All I ever want to do anymore is eat or sleep, and since I've already eaten . . ." She shrugged, leaving the rest unsaid. "Come on, Jake," she exhorted her husband, walking firmly to the coat closet to retrieve her jacket. "I can hardly keep my eyes open."

Jake looked at his wife with puzzled crossness, but he didn't say what was on his mind, which was that his wife had developed a lamentable penchant for tall tales recently. He got his own jacket and followed Rosie out the door, accompanied by Ross and Ellen. Ross was looking thoughtful and Ellen was looking woebegone, and Jake found himself shaking his head at the peculiarities his spouse and best friends were exhibiting all of a sudden. But he was not to be left in the dark for long, because even as Ellen and Ross were waving them good-bye, Rosie could be seen talking his ear off while Jake kept turning his head toward her again and again listening avidly.

Ellen started to turn away and go back in the house, and Ross caught her hand. She looked up at him warily, then with puzzlement as she saw the warm look of regard in his eyes. That look had been missing lately, and she was a little nervous about what could be behind it now.

"Why don't I bring in some wood and start a fire, break open a bottle of wine . . ." Ross shrugged, tugging at an errant strand of Ellen's hair. He saw the hesitancy in her eyes and added gently, "We need to talk, Ellen. Let's do it comfortably."

"All . . . right," Ellen said slowly, suddenly longing for the warmth of Ross's intimacy. She was missing him badly, but until now she hadn't admitted it to herself. Still, she was half afraid their talking would destroy intimacy between them rather than enhance it, and as she went to get the wine and two glasses, she was actively praying that the two of them could find some common ground of agreement and get back to what they'd shared before that damned barn had gotten in their way!

Ross fussed with the fire, getting it just right, while Ellen sat back on the sofa and sipped her wine, wondering if he was as reluctant as she was to break up the pleasant atmosphere. Finally, however, he came to sit beside her, took the glass of wine she offered, and leaned back, stretching his legs out to the blaze, his eyes half hooded with lazy contentment.

Out of the blue he murmured, "Just how rich are you, wife?"

It was a calmly, almost lazily delivered question, but Ellen, startled at hearing it at all, had to take a moment to gather her thoughts before she could answer. When she did, she saw Ross jerk, then swing two astonished blue eyes in her direction. "You aren't serious?!" he breathed.

Ellen merely nodded, her eyes wide as she studied Ross, wondering why he was so surprised. Then she realized she had never actually told him the amount of her bank account, and perhaps that was part of the trouble. He must have thought she wasn't as well off as she was.

Ross turned back to stare at the flames, and she heard a softly drawn, "Whew!" Then a little louder, "My God! I never dreamed . . ." And then he fell silent again, shaking his head in wonderment.

"Does it . . . ah . . . upset you, Ross?" Ellen ventured hesitantly, suddenly realizing her palms were wet with nervousness.

He turned his head to look at her and gave a sort of

bemused shrug. "Upset me?" he repeated. He closed his eyes momentarily, and when he opened them again there was laughter in the clear blue depths. "Hell, no, it doesn't upset me! Do I look crazy?"

Ellen ventured a hesitant smile in return. "Maybe around the edges a little," she said solemnly. "But mainly you look sane."

"Which edges?" Ross asked, taking mock offense.

"That one," Ellen suggested, stroking a finger over his mustache, enjoying the feel of it with longing wistfulness. "I think I read somewhere that only crazy people wear mustaches," she lied solemnly.

"Huh!" Ross objected, stroking a fond finger over the growth on his lip. "Whoever wrote that must have been the one who's crazy." He took her hand in his and played tantalizingly with her fingers then. "Crazy or not though, I'm sane enough to know when I owe my wife an apology."

Ellen held her breath for a moment, everything inside her stilled with waiting for him to go on, to show her he did love her, that he needed her!

"I'm a stiff-necked, stubborn, son-of-a—" Ross hesitated, looking up at her mischievously. "Well, let's just say I don't show good sense sometimes, Ellen," he amended his self-castigation without groveling in the least. "I'm sorry if I hurt you, made you feel like you weren't as important as you are to me." He went on then, hesitantly, to explain what had been on his mind, just as he had told it to Rosie, though with a great deal more loving inflection. And then he finished by asking, "Want to help me build a barn, Ellen? And there's a new bull I've been wanting to buy, and some more land on the south side of what I own, and . . ."

Ellen stopped his mischievous teasing firmly, her heart

swelling with her love for him. "The land *who* owns?" she corrected him sternly.

Ross looked as meek as he was able to, which wasn't saying much. "The land *we* own, Mrs. Sayer," he said mildly. "I can picture you now," he went on in an expansive tone, "the cattle and land queen of Kansas. Maybe we ought to branch out to Texas," he added musingly. "There's more scope there for . . ."

"Ross!" Ellen warned him crossly, wanting him to shut up and kiss her and then take her right there in front of the fire in their own living room on their ranch.

"Yes, dear?" he asked deferentially. "Did you want something?"

She certainly did, and she told him so without mincing words. Ross pretended to look shocked, then grudgingly started to take her into his arms. "You mean I have to pay for the barn like this?" he complained sulkily.

"Pronto!" Ellen informed him with impatient firmness, lifting her lips for the kiss she wanted so badly.

But Ross held back, studying her expectant mouth interestedly. "Where'd you *get* that much money?" he asked with a touch of awe.

Sighing, Ellen drew back, unpursing her lips. "I had the good fortune . . . I *think,*" she amended crossly, "to be the only surviving relative of a parsimonious, stubborn, crotchety old bachelor who seemed to have been a genius at playing the stockmarket as well! Now it seems, I'm paying for that by ending up married to a stubborn, crotchety old . . ."

Ross broke in hastily. ". . . rancher who's a genius at making love." He started to give her the kiss she'd been waiting for then, but Ellen held back.

"You couldn't prove it by me," she pouted. "I can't even get a kiss from the love genius, much less—"

"You could if you'd shut up," Ross growled laughingly,

then proceeded to do it for her, quite forcefully, by placing his mouth firmly over hers.

Ellen's response was so wholeheartedly enthusiastic that after a few minutes, Ross drew back, searching her eyes with his own warmly loving ones, and said, "Rosie told me women can't separate their heads from their bodies. I seem to be getting the message that I'm forgiven. Is that right?"

Ellen stretched deliciously in his arms, molding herself eagerly to his lithe frame. "Completely," she murmured in between hungry little kisses all over his face. "Would you like a further demonstration?"

"Ummm . . ." Ross assented, shifting to lie back on the sofa and pulling her on top of him. "I'm a sucker for demonstrations. You should see me at the state fair. I . . ."

It was Ellen's turn to shut him up, and she did so with a great deal of enjoyment, then proceeded to demonstrate her forgiveness to her heart's content. Once, in the middle of the demonstration, however, a sudden thought struck her, and she lifted her head from her nuzzling of Ross's now bare chest to say abjectly, "Ross, I need forgiving too. I hate to admit it, but I have a rotten temper. I shouldn't have flown off at you like that."

He groaned at having his total concentration on Ellen's most satisfactory ministrations interrupted and muttered, "I see what you're up to. You're just saying that so I'll have to demonstrate my forgiveness too. Lazy witch!"

"That would be nice, too, of course," Ellen murmured with a complacent grin before she sobered again. "*Do* you forgive me, Ross?" she asked seriously.

He sighed heavily, and with much forbearance and patience decided to reassure her in exactly the way she had been reassuring him until Ellen was so completely convinced, she was begging him to show a little mercy

169

. . . one way or another. Happily, his idea of mercy coincided with hers, and their resulting union was a sweetly hot reunion of two starved individuals into one united, satisfied couple.

CHAPTER FOURTEEN

Ellen sat slowly rocking, drowsy with contentment, staring out the window at a March snowstorm that was blanketing the surrounding countryside in enchanting white. She patted her slightly rounded tummy, feeling absolutely tiptop mentally and physically, and gazed down fondly at the swell of her abdomen.

"Daddy will be home soon wanting his supper," she informed her unhearing offspring, talking to him—she already knew it was a *him* with some inner knowledge she didn't question—as though he would be interested in hearing that his as yet unknown father would soon be home. "I suppose I'd better fix it," she added lazily, making no move to get up from her comfortable chair.

A few moments later she realized she'd left it too late when she heard the back door open and close, then a stomping sound as Ross cleaned his feet. "Oops!" she said mildly, then, realizing Ross was coming in early because of the storm, she relaxed and waited for him where she was, thinking craftily that she might be able to coerce him into helping her fix dinner.

He came into the room and smiled when he saw the welcoming light in Ellen's eyes. "It's getting bad out there," he informed her as he doffed his coat, then came to kiss her hello. "Thought I'd come in early and curl up by the fire with my fat wife."

"Insults won't get you any supper," Ellen responded with a disapproving sniff. "Besides, fat has its uses. I notice you snuggle up close now that the nights are cold."

"Ha!" Ross tossed back lazily, stretching his arms up in a powerful movement to ease their tiredness. "Doesn't look like I'm going to get any supper anyway," he said, giving her a mock disapproving scowl. "And as for snuggling up at night, I don't have much choice. You take up the whole bed now." He grinned wickedly as he leaned over her, placing his hands on the arms of the chair and trapping her where she sat. "Besides, if I keep you close, I can dodge those cold feet of yours."

Ellen pretended to take offense. "I can always try to find my pink fuzzies again if my feet bother you," she informed him sternly.

"No, you can't. I threw them away," Ross said, unperturbed. Then he gazed down at her stomach fondly. "How's Junior?"

"Junior's as snug as a bug in a rug," Ellen smiled. "He's in a good spot to wait out the storm."

"And how's Mama?" Ross asked, raising his head to look lovingly into her eyes.

"Mama's feeling lazy," Ellen informed him mischievously. "She doesn't want to cook Daddy's supper."

"Then she doesn't have to," Ross answered, surprising her with his sweet generosity. "But there'll be a price," he added, more true to form.

"I knew it!" Ellen snorted, scowling at him. "What is it this time?"

"Not much," he said innocently, stretching out one hand to trace the new fullness of Ellen's breasts. "On a bad day like this, a lot of businessmen take the opportunity to take inventory."

"And what were you thinking of inventorying?" Ellen said with dry suspicion.

172

"Mama," Ross answered with a grin, then shushed her instinctive scolding. "Just a partial inventory," he said gravely, beginning to undo the buttons of her top. "They tell me this may not last, and I want to enjoy it while I can."

Ellen giggled, enjoying with languorous contentment and a delicious, unurgent arousal Ross's inspection of her increased attributes. Finally, he bent his head to place lazy, seeking kisses on the smooth skin of her breasts where they swelled above her bra, then straightened up, gesturing at himself where he had done a little swelling of his own.

"Fat ladies turn me on," he said simply.

"Good," Ellen retorted. "I don't want to catch you with any thin ones until about July."

"Narrowminded," he muttered with a sniff as he headed for the kitchen. "What do you want for supper? Keeping in mind my limited skills, of course."

"Anything will do," Ellen said easily, going back to her rocking and filled to overflowing with a sense of well-being. She daydreamed for a while, heard the phone ring, and frowned, not wanting to get up, then settled down when it stopped and she realized Ross had picked it up in the kitchen.

Ten minutes later Ross entered the room, and though he seemed much as usual, Ellen noted with puzzlement that there was something different about him. "I have to go out for a while," he said overcasually. "A neighbor down the road needs some help with a calving."

"Oh, Ross, no," Ellen said sympathetically. "And on such a bad night too."

He shrugged. "It doesn't matter. There's some soup and a grilled cheese sandwich ready for you in the kitchen." He moved to pick up his coat and shrug into it, and Ellen wondered where her sudden sense of unease came from.

173

"Aren't you going to eat?" she asked worriedly as she got up from her chair to accompany him to the door.

"I'll eat when I get back," he said, again too casually, though Ellen told herself she was imagining things.

"Will you be long?" she asked, anxious about having him go out into the storm.

"Can't tell," he answered, a touch of impatience in his voice that puzzled Ellen even further. "I'll see you when I can. If I'm not back by bedtime, go on to sleep without me."

"Fine," Ellen said, her voice low, perhaps betraying some of the mixed emotions she was feeling.

"Honey . . ." Ross turned back to her and took her shoulders into his hands. "I'll be all right. No need to worry."

He sounded more normal, and Ellen relaxed somewhat. "All right," she said, smiling at him. He returned the smile, though his eyes looked somewhat abstracted, then he kissed her and opened the door.

Ellen watched as he trudged across the yard to his pickup, climbed in and gunned the motor, then started off down the road in a mist of white snow. She closed the door and wandered to the kitchen to eat the food he'd prepared, wishing she didn't feel this awful sense of something about to happen, though it wasn't strong enough to upset her too much. It was just a nagging, persistent itch that wouldn't leave her alone.

After she'd eaten, she cleared up the kitchen, then settled to some knitting before the television set and had just started to become interested in a documentary when the phone rang again. A little dart of alarm went through her at the sound, but she told herself she was a complete ninny, and she rose to take the call, feeling cross with herself.

She barely had time to say hello before a crisp, efficient, and very sexy female voice asked, "Ross Sayer, please."

"He isn't here right now," Ellen answered in a puzzled tone, since she didn't recognize the voice. "This is Mrs. Sayer. May I . . ."

But the woman, apparently distracted by something, seemed to hear only the first part of Ellen's reply. "Oh, he's already left then? Good . . ." and then hastily, as there was more distraction in the background, "Thank you . . . good-bye!" followed by the click of the phone and a dial tone and Ellen's glaring stare at the telephone.

"Now *who* was that?" she muttered crossly as she replaced the receiver and continued to contemplate it as though she wanted it to answer her question. The woman had sounded as though she knew Ross was going somewhere this evening, as though he was *expected* somewhere, and yet Ellen knew that the voice on the phone wasn't the voice of their neighbor's wife, so it couldn't be someone from the neighboring farm; there was no one else there! Besides, Ross had had ample time to get there if, in fact, that was actually where he was going!

Pacing distractedly now, Ellen scoffed at her own suspicious mind. Ross loved her. She knew he did. And he had no reason to lie to her about where he was going either! She was simply letting her imagination run wild. It must be her pregnancy making her prey to these idiotic thoughts.

Determinedly, she sat back down to her knitting and the television to spend the rest of the evening with her ear cocked for Ross's return and fighting an unaccountable depression when he didn't. About eleven P.M., she went to the bedroom, intending to go to sleep, concentrating on how much she trusted Ross, but the sight of her now slightly ungainly figure in the mirror made her gloomily

175

175

aware that her appeal was somewhat less than it had been and would get a lot worse before it got better again.

By one A.M., after lying sleepless for two hours, and with Ross nowhere in sight, Ellen got up again and went to fix herself a cup of hot cocoa, which she sipped at unenthusiastically as she paced back and forth and tried to quell her growing concern.

By three A.M., Ellen was almost frantic, her worst fears gaining strength by the moment and her hurt growing by leaps and bounds. Finally, she came to a stop in front of the telephone and her hand was half out to pick it up, when she drew it back reluctantly. The early hours of the morning was not the best time to call up a neighbor and ask casually after the whereabouts of one's husband!

"Suppose I just drive over there," she muttered to herself self-consciously. If Ross and the neighbor were in the barn with the calf, she would be able to tell from the road. Ross's pickup would be parked where she could see it, and the barn was close enough to the road to see if there were any lights there.

Telling herself she had every right to check on her own husband's well-being, Ellen dressed warmly and left the house. The snow had slackened, though flakes were still coming down, and Ellen drove with automatic care the short distance to the neighbors', only to find that Ross's pickup was nowhere in sight and the whole place was wrapped in a dark mantle that matched her rapidly deteriorating mood.

She retraced the road back to the house, the car slipping a little on the icy surface, and that made her wonder if Ross had perhaps had an accident. Perhaps he had to go into town for something and had slipped off the road on the way.

This time she fairly flew to the phone to dial the local hospital with trembling fingers. Moments later she sat

176

slumped in dejection when she was informed that no one of Ross's name or description had been admitted that night. She tried to tell herself she should be grateful that Ross was apparently alive and well, but by now she was in such a mood to kill him herself, she found it hard to convince herself she was glad he wasn't hurt.

But maybe he *was* hurt! she thought an instant later, freezing where she sat as a picture of Ross lying off the road somewhere bleeding and helpless rose in her mind. Instantly, she was out of the chair and back out of the house. She climbed into the car, backed it carefully, and started off down the road, her eyes searching anxiously for any sign that Ross's pickup had left the road and was lying somewhere with him pinned in it.

There was absolutely nothing to tell her that such was the case, however, and she had reached town before she realized she was a fool on a fool's errand. Wherever Ross Sayer was, he was most likely not only alive and well but probably enjoying himself in a way that was going to earn him a place in the hospital that had nothing to do with any automobile accident.

Hardly realizing what she was doing, Ellen automatically made her way to Rosie's house for comfort and advice, not even remarking the unusual fact that it was ablaze with lights at this time of the morning. She went to the door to ring the bell, and when no one came to answer it, she tried the knob, feeling gratified that it turned in her hand. At least *something* worked on this godawful night, she consoled herself with angry self-pity.

The downstairs was as quiet as a tomb, and Ellen debated about going upstairs to wake Rosie from a sound sleep to listen to her own troubles. She glanced at her watch to find that it was now five A.M., and thinking Rosie would be up in a couple of hours anyway, Ellen settled herself on the couch to contemplate her suddenly disastrous future

177

with silent tears and inner wailings against the man who could be so cruel as to put her through such anguish when she was carrying his child and when she loved him to distraction.

At last, she cried herself to sleep, slumped into a heap on the sofa, and the next thing she knew, she was being shaken awake by a perfectly livid Ross, whose expression showed clearly he thought *he* was the one due explanations and apologies.

"Wake up, Ellen!" he practically snarled at her, making her blink up at him with groggy astonishment at his tone. Then she remembered where she was, and, more important, *why* she was there, and she drew back from his less than gentle shaking with a snarl of her own.

"Don't touch me, you . . . you lying cheat!" she shouted at him, scrambling out of his way, huddling into the sofa cushions to glare up at him.

Ross drew back and straightened, his expression thunderous and puzzled at the same time. "What the hell are you talking about?" he yelled back at her. "And why aren't you home where you belong?!"

"Ha!" Ellen glowered at him contemptuously. "You'd like that, wouldn't you?" And at Ross's angry, puzzled stare, she added, "It would suit you just fine to have a dumb, stupid wife who stays home barefoot and pregnant while you chase after women all night, wouldn't it?"

At that, Ross looked incredulous, then concerned. "Have you gone crazy?" he asked with astonished exasperation.

A hesitant cough sounded behind him, and, for the first time, Ellen noted Jake hovering in the background. "I told you you ought to tell her," Jake informed Ross helpfully, then hastily turned his attention back to Ellen when Ross glared at him in a way that told him his helpfulness had gone unappreciated. "Ross was with me last night, Ellen,"

178

Jake hurriedly informed Ellen. "Rosie went into labor, I panicked, and called Ross and he didn't want to tell you because he was afraid you'd want to come with him." He hesitated while Ross glared at him and Ellen stared at him in open-mouthed astonishment, then a reluctant grin stretched his mouth. "It was a girl," he said softly. "We're going to name her Mary Ellen. Mary after my mother and Ellen after you." Then he stood back grinning all over his face as Ellen launched herself to her feet and threw herself into his arms.

"Oh, Jake!" Ellen yelled happily. "I'm so glad! Is Rosie all right? Is the baby okay? Are *you* all right?"

"I'm fine . . . everybody's fine." Jake laughed, returning her joyous hug. Then he saw Ross still glowering at the two of them over Ellen's shoulder, and his laughter became slyer and more subdued. "Everybody's fine but your husband, that is. I think I'd better go make some coffee while you two get straightened out."

But at mention of Ross, Ellen's joy turned to anger again, and she swung on her heel to glare up at her husband. "Why didn't you tell me?" she demanded heatedly. "How could you leave me sitting there all night wondering where in the hell you were?!" She marched up to a still angry Ross, her scowl mutinous. "And who was that woman who called asking for you last night?" she challenged threateningly.

"What woman?" Ross snapped, his demeanor indicating he wasn't prepared to give an inch. "I don't know anything about some woman calling you!"

Again, Jake coughed gently. "It was probably a nurse at the hospital," he informed the two of them placatingly. "I was so distracted, I asked her to give you a call to see if you'd left yet."

Ellen closed her eyes, then opened them to show that they still contained fire as she gritted out, "She didn't tell

179

me who she was. She just asked if you were there, then acted glad to know you were on your way to . . . wherever!"

Ross's jaw tightened as he stared stonily down at her. "And you immediately jumped to the conclusion I was on my way to a hot affair! So much for trust!"

"I *did* trust you!" Ellen snarled, stamping her foot in frustration. "I trusted you right up until three thirty this morning when you hadn't come back, you hadn't called, and I drove to the neighbors to find you weren't there!" She faced him with all her remembered hurt and anger in every line of her body. "I even trusted you then!" she informed him nastily. "I thought you might have had an accident and I went home and called the hospital. You weren't there either! Then I thought you might be lying on the side of the road hurt and I drove that damned road with my heart in my mouth expecting any moment to find you dead or dying!"

Tears welled up in Ellen's eyes as she let her emotion get the better of her, and she didn't know if it was that or her confessions that finally softened Ross's anger. At any rate, something did, and he took a step toward her, his rugged face becoming gentler with regret.

"Stop right there!" Ellen snapped. "I want to know why you didn't tell me about Rosie!"

Ross sighed and raked a hand over his tired face. "Because I was afraid you'd do exactly what you did," he informed her, a trace of exasperation returning to his voice. "I didn't want you out on those icy roads in such bad weather and I didn't want you staying up all night worrying about Rosie! I figured I'd wake you up this morning with the good news."

Far from alleviating her anger, Ross's protectiveness infuriated Ellen. "*You* figured!" she yelled at him. "*You* figured!" she repeated angrily. "Ross Sayer, when are you going to learn that I'm not some breakable doll but a real live woman who has as much right to know and do things as you do! You're an insufferable male chauvinist pig!"

Her criticism stiffened Ross's back and his expression grew thunderous again. "And you're a stubborn tomboy who doesn't have sense enough to appreciate a man who wants to treat you like a woman," he flared at her angrily.

"Oh!" Ellen wailed, her lower lip sticking out as Ross found the one place to strike where she was most vulnerable. She still had occasional doubts about whether Ross found her as femininely attractive as he had Tina, and she had worked hard throughout their marriage so far to satisfy both her own inclinations toward tomboyishness and her belief that Ross wanted a china doll instead of a fully rounded woman. Now he was saying she had failed. "You fink!" she burst out in a renewed bout of tears. "You don't seem to mind when I work like a cowhand on that precious ranch!" She struggled to say more, failed, and flung herself away from Ross to run up the stairs and collapse upon the nearest bed where she lay shuddering with sobs.

She was reduced to hiccuping misery by the time he came into the room to sit down beside her and run a comforting hand over her back. "Ellen . . ." He started to talk to her in a soothing tone, but she jerked herself away and heard him sigh with resignation. Then he neatly flipped her over onto her back and pinned her against the mattress with enough force to keep her where she was, glaring up at him, but not enough force to hurt her.

"Listen to me, wife," he said with firm determination. "I'm very, very sorry I put you through all that. I had no idea you would even know I was gone so long. I thought you'd go to sleep without worrying."

"Ha!" Ellen sulked at him resentfully. "It just so happens I *can't* sleep when you're not in bed with me!" She was both chagrined that her revelation was less a weapon for her than for Ross and infuriated when it brought a complacent grin to his handsome face.

"I didn't know that," he said in a wondering, satisfied tone that made Ellen even angrier.

"Well, you do now!" she snarled at him. "But that isn't the point anyway. The point is you still haven't learned what real femininity is all about!" She faltered, then added with pitiful woebegoneness, "Maybe you'd be happier with someone like Tina than with me. I guess I'm too masculine for you."

Ross's clear blue eyes widened as he stared down at the soft, trembling femininity he held in his arms, and then as understanding dawned, he curved his lips into a tender smile. "Oh, no," he said softly. "You're not the least bit masculine, Mrs. Sayer. And I wouldn't be happy with anyone in the world but you."

Ellen eyed him longingly, becoming somewhat mollified by the light of love in his eyes and the tenderness in his tone. "You don't act like it sometimes," she sniffed self-pityingly, but in a softer, less abrasive tone.

"Sometimes I'm a complete idiot," Ross agreed in a mild tone that was soothingly comforting. "But if you'll keep teaching me what a woman is, I promise you I'll do better at learning."

"Well, there's just a few things left for you to learn," Ellen said in a small voice approaching forgiveness.

"Such as like learning to treat you like an adult instead of a brainless beauty," Ross suggested helpfully, his tone suspiciously sober.

"Yes," Ellen replied firmly, hoping to flatten what she suspected was a tendency toward amusement in Ross's gleaming blue eyes. "If you can accept my help on the ranch, why can't you accept my doing other things that you mistakenly consider unfeminine?"

"Honey, there's not a doubt in my mind that you're all

182

woman," Ross answered, and this time his soberness had the ring of sincerity. "But if you ever expect me to reach a stage where I don't want to protect you, where I don't consider you weaker in some ways than I am, and happy to have it so, then I don't think we're ever going to reach an understanding on this point."

Ellen gazed at him, trying to understand what he was really saying, and then beginning to smile as she did begin to understand. But just to clarify matters, she questioned him. "You don't think I'm a dumb female?" she challenged quietly.

"I never met anyone smarter," Ross answered solemnly.

"You don't think I'm too . . . er . . . mannish?" she asked hesitatingly.

Ross moved his hand to her breast and stroked tantalizingly. "I never knew a man who felt like this," he teased with quiet satisfaction.

"You like me better than Tina?" Ellen then asked in a small voice, eyeing him anxiously.

"Infinitely," Ross answered with tender sincerity. "There's no comparison."

"Good," Ellen breathed on a satisfied sigh. Then she drew back and eyed Ross fiercely. "But don't ever, ever lie to me again, Ross Sayer! Not to protect me or for any other reason!"

"I won't," Ross promised solemnly, moving to seal his promise with a hard kiss. Then he raised his head, and his voice had grown thicker when he said, "Let's go home, honey. I need some lessons in what a real woman does with all that femininity."

Ellen nodded eagerly, then stopped and began to shake her head no, causing Ross to frown. "Not yet," Ellen soothed his impatience. "I have to eat something first and then I want to go see Rosie's baby."

"Eat?" Ross said, puzzled by her thinking of something so mundane at a time like this.

"Yes, eat!" Ellen said urgently, scrambling to her feet. "You don't realize what a glutton your son is! If I don't feed him regularly, he gets downright nasty, just like his father!" She hurried to the door, then turned back to frown at Ross impatiently when he still lay lounging on the bed.

"So it's going to be a boy, is it?" he asked with a pleased smile.

"Yes," Ellen verified, utter certainty in her tone. "And I swear, I don't know what I'm going to do if he turns out to be a carbon copy of you! He'll have me in heaven one minute and in hell the next!"

Ross laughed and got to his feet to cross to her and wrap his arms around her waist. "You can take it," he said confidently. "After all, the heaven's worth it, isn't it?"

"Maybe," Ellen admitted grudgingly. "But it's hard to remember that when I'm in hell."

Ross laughed again, throwing back his head and letting it out with joyous abandon. In the middle of it a knock sounded on the door, and Ross glanced at the door mischievously, toning his laughter down to a chuckle. "I'll bet that's Jake wondering what in the hell we're laughing about when a few minutes ago we were fighting like a couple of boxers facing off."

"*You're* laughing, I'm not," Ellen said with fond crossness, skirting him to fling the door open. Sure enough, Jake stood there, his eyes dancing with curiosity.

"Jake, I'm hungry," Ellen said authoritatively. "I'm going downstairs to fix us some breakfast."

"Worked up an appetite, did you?" Jake chuckled complacently. "Well, so did I, so make it a big breakfast, Ellie. I missed my dinner last night."

Ross snorted his disbelief, remembering the inroads

Jake had made on the contents of a snack machine in the hospital waiting room. Jake heard the sound, managed a wounded look, and said, "Well, I had to have something to keep up my strength!" and turned away to stalk down the stairs with offended dignity.

Ellen looked up at her husband disapprovingly. "Now you've hurt his feelings!" she whispered.

Ross grinned and shook his head. "Don't worry. Once he's digging into the breakfast you're going to fix and talking his head off about Rosie and the baby, he'll forget everything else."

Ellen smiled and nodded. "You're right," she agreed. "But you two do the talking. I'm going to be eating too!"

Sometime later, after breakfast had been eaten and a trip to the hospital had produced oohs and aahs of delight from Ellen at viewing the tiny mite whose father beamed proudly at her through the viewing glass, Ellen and Ross finally made their way home, both of them yawning and beginning to sag a little after a night devoid of sleep.

Once inside the house, however, Ellen turned to Ross and slid her arms up around his neck. "I guess you want me to show you I forgive you again, right?" she said slyly, managing to accidentally unfasten the top button of his shirt.

"You forgive *me*?" Ross growled, slapping her hand away from his buttons. "How about the other way around? I'm the one who has been accused of everything from infidelity to mental cruelty!"

Ellen sighed and adopted a martyred look. "Oh, all right," she said with injured patience, lifting Ross's hands to her buttons. "If you insist, you can show me you forgive me."

Ross glared at her for an instant before the glare dissolved into an anticipatory grin, and he took over the job of unbuttoning Ellen's top without prompting. "That's

185

very big of you," he punned, leering down at her swollen breasts and slightly protruding tummy.

Ellen sighed and eyed him with loving forbearance. "You know, Ross," she advised him tolerantly, "you not only have a rotten temper, but your sense of humor could use a little work too."

"But you love me anyway, right?" he asked with smug self-confidence, divesting her of the top and placing eager hands on the snap of her bra.

She nodded. "Somebody has to," she agreed on a sigh. "And it was just my luck that you redeemed yourself in my eyes right when I found out I was ready to love again."

"Redeemed myself!" he snorted, turning her firmly toward the bedroom. "I was always a sterling example of American manhood. You were just too prejudiced to notice my fine qualities."

"Maybe so," Ellen replied doubtfully, casting a sceptical eye back at him over her shoulder. "But I'll bet you didn't learn how to wrestle with a female in the backseat of a van by always being a squeaky clean American boy."

Ross gave her a smugly wicked grin as he shut the bedroom door firmly behind him and gestured toward the bed. "Those were my training days," he said, waving her peremptorily to finish undressing and await his pleasure in their bed. "If I hadn't gone through that apprenticeship, I would never have been able to shake you up so much when it was *your* turn in the backseat of a van."

He ignored her look of disbelief at his conceit and started undressing, while Ellen finished her own, and when he joined her in the bed, snug and warm under the covers, he pulled her into his arms with some of that technique he boasted about and which Ellen silently agreed was superior.

"Now, wife," he purred against her mouth. "How about if we take forgiveness for granted and indulge in a little

186

experimentation with that femininity you're so worried about."

Ellen chuckled slyly, stretching herself with pleasure under his knowing hands. "I'm not worried about it anymore," she cooed complacently. "You've already told me I'm all woman."

"Ummm," Ross agreed, caressing her full breasts with warm, kneading fingers. "You certainly are. Let's see, you have two of these . . ." And he bent to kiss what he held with seeking lips, causing Ellen to shiver deliciously under his mouth. "And this . . ." He moved lower to search out her navel with his tongue. "And this . . ." he added thickly, one hand caressing her inner thigh, then traveling up to cup the throbbing center of her need, wringing a groan from Ellen's parted lips.

"Those are yours, not mine," Ellen gasped, shuddering beneath his touch. "All yours, Ross, always."

"I know," he agreed with husky possessiveness. "And this belongs to you . . ." He guided her hand to his own need, which Ellen took into her keeping with a stroking, seductive possessiveness of her own.

"Oh, Ross . . ." Ellen breathed, accepting his kiss of gratitude with sweet eagerness. And when he raised his head, she looked into his eyes with all her love shining from hers. "Let's share what we have . . . now, please. I love you. I want you so very much."

"It's time to love?" he asked, his amusement tempered by the passionate arousal and love encompassing her in the light from his clear blue eyes.

"It's time to love . . ." Ellen agreed from deep in her throat, ending on a moan of satisfaction as Ross did share everything he had with her, then and from that moment on.

Come Faith, Come Fire

Vanessa Royall

Proud as her aristocratic upbringing, bold as the
ancient gypsy blood that ran in her veins, the
beautiful golden-haired Maria saw her family burned
at the stake and watched her young love, forced into
the priesthood. Desperate and bound by a forbidden
love, Maria defies the Grand Inquisitor himself and
flees across Spain to a burning love that was destined
to be free! $2.95

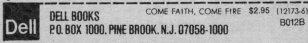

THE DARK HORSEMAN

Marianne Harvey
author of *The Proud Hunter*

Beautiful Donna Penroze had sworn to her
dying father that she would save her sole legacy, the crumbling tin mines and the ancient,
desolate estate *Trencobban*. But the mines
were failing, and Donna had no one to turn to.
No one except the mysterious Nicholas Tre-
varvas—rich, arrogant, commanding. Donna
would do anything but surrender her pride, anything but admit her irresistible longing for *The
Dark Horseman.*

A Dell Book $3.50